NIGHT PICNIC

Journal of Literature and Art

VOLUME 5, ISSUE 3

Night Picnic Press LLC
New York, New York
October 2022

NIGHT PICNIC: Journal of Literature and Art   Volume 5, Issue 3 • October 2022

Igor V. Zaitsev, *Founder, Publisher, and Editor-in-Chief*
Gordon Stumpo, *Managing Editor and Art Director*
Oksana Williams, *Editor*

editor@nightpicnic.net
www.nightpicnic.net

Night Picnic is a journal of literature and art. We accept novels, novellas, plays, short and flash stories, fairytales and fantasy for adults, poetry, interviews, essays (including popular science essays), letters to the editors, and artwork. Previously published work cannot be considered (this include blogs, Facebook, Wattpad, etc). Published triannually in February, June, and October by Night Picnic Press LLC. Established in 2018. We are grateful for donations of any amount. They support the publication of the journal.

For single print copies ($15) and digital versions ($5), please go to www.amazon.com and the Kindle store. Subscriptions to Night Picnic Journal are $35 (3 issues), $45 for libraries. Foreign orders, please add $10. Subscriptions are only available by mail through Night Picnic Press LLC. Using the subscription form on **page 123**, please send checks or money orders to:

Night Picnic Press LLC
P.O. Box 3819
New York, NY 10163-3819

ISSN 2639-7625 (Paperback)   ISBN 978-1-970033-25-0 (Paperback)
ISSN 2639-7633 (eBook)   ISBN 978-1-970033-26-7 (eBook)

NIGHT PICNIC • Volume 5, Issue 3 • October 2022

CONTENTS

AUTHORS AND EDITORS

FICTION

POETRY

PLAYS

AUTHORS AND EDITORS

Acuff, Gale. Poet. University professor in the US, China, and Palestine. Widely published in national and international literary journals. Author of three books of poetry: *Buffalo Nickel, The Weight of the World,* and *The Story of My Lives.* Zababdeh, Palestine.

Alper, David M. Educator. Forthcoming poetry collection is *Hush.* Published in *Oxford Magazine* and *Invisible City.* New York, NY, USA.

Baughfman, Evan. Playwright. Horror writer. Dedicated library patron. Author of funny and spooky stuff. Long Beach, CA, USA.

de Winter, RC. Poet. Digital artist. Anthologized in numerous collections, including *Uno, Verian Thomas,* and *New York City Haiku, NY Times.* Pushcart Prize nominee: 2019, 2020, and 2022. Fairfield, CT, USA.

Dowling, Joseph J. Owner of a small chain of retro-arcade bars. He has garnered several recent acceptances and will appear in several upcoming anthologies. London, UK.

Fantuzzi, Massimo. British-Italian. Educator. Editorial board member at *Triggerfish Critical Review.* Author of *Marcia Gioie.* Published in *Alba, Bombay Gin, Danse Macabre, Poetry Salzburg Review, Grey Sparrow Journal, Menacing Hedge, The Honest Ulsterman, Straylight, Orbis,* and elsewhere. Leicestershire, England, UK.

Gambone, Philip. Writer. Retired teacher of English and writing at Boston University Academy and Harvard Extension School. Author of five books of fiction and nonfiction. Boston, MA, USA.

Hadin, Christopher. Writer. Naturalist. Educator. Published in *Sky Island Journal* and *The Thieving Magpie.* Ferndale, MI, USA.

Hogan, Michael Paul. Poet, fiction writer and literary essayist. Published extensively in the USA, UK, India, and China. London, UK.

Jewett, Rollin. Playwriter. Screenwriter. Author. Singer-Songwriter. Published in numerous journals & anthologies, several plays and films produced, noted short story writer/author, and award-winning singer, songwriter. Holly Springs, NC, USA.

Landey, Lee. Writer. Musician. Author of one book of short fiction. Los Angeles, CA, USA.

Mestrovic, Ivana. Poet. Studio manager for sculptor Mark di Suvero. Published in *Brief Wilderness, Cider Press Review, Doubly Mad, Evening Street Review, The Opiate, Oxidant Engine, Plainsongs, Slant,* and *Visitant Lit.* Long Island City, NY, USA.

Risemberg, Richard. Writer. Photographer. Published in numerous literary journals on three continents. Los Angeles, CA, USA.

Scharf, Mark. Playwright. Actor. Teacher. Plays published in *Pioneer Drama, Original Works Publishing, Brooklyn Publishing, Heurer Publishing, Green Room Press. Meriwether Publishing,* and *Stage Rights,* a Broadway Licensing imprint. Baltimore, MD, USA.

Stumpo, Gordon. Managing Editor & Art Director of *Night Picnic*. Published scholar, writer, and illustrator. Mentor. Educator. Fashion designer. New York, NY, USA.

Townsend, Charles. Writer. Hiker. Undergraduate student at UMass Amherst. Longmeadow, MA, USA.

Williams, Oksana. Editor of *Night Picnic*. Bibliophile. Graduate of Irkutsk State Polytechnical University and math teacher of the American International School of Bucharest. Bucharest, Romania.

Zaitsev, Igor V. Founder, publisher, and editor-in-chief of *Night Picnic*. Biologist. Poet. Writer. Professor at Borough of Manhattan Community College, the City University of New York. New York, NY, USA.

PAST CONTRIBUTING AUTHORS

Edward Ahern
Penel Alden
Angelica Allain
Samuel J. Allen
Douglas Balmain
Ariel Berry
Mads Bohan
Francesca Della Bona
A. C. Bohleber
Tori Bryl
David Capps
Frank Carellini
Grant Carriker
Natalie K. Christiansen
Robert Ciesla
Tim Connors
Kalynn Michelle Cotton
Mary Eliza Crane
Tanner Cremeans
Kaier Curtin
Alex Dako
Holly Day
John Delaney
Shane Delaney
Lenny DellaRocca
RC de Winter
Frank Diamond
Leslie Dianne
William Doreski
Karen Downs-Barton
Gary Duehr
Michael Dubilet
Emily Dupuis
Tonya Eberhard
Alan Elyshevitz
E. W. Farnsworth
Jonathan Ferrini
Fayette Fox
Cass Francis
Roberta Hartling Gates
TeaJae Glennon
Rich Glinnen
D. C. Gonk
Julian Grant
Gerri R. Gray
John Grey
Jordan M. Griffin
Max Halper
Marcus Hansson
Spencer Harrington
Colton Heitzman-Breen
Bryan E. Helton
Laura E. Hoffman
Jery Hollis

Brent Holmes
J.D. Hosemann
Briley D. Jones
Steve Karamitros
Mark Keane
Mark Kessinger
Harry Kidd
Steven Kish
Jacob Klein
Hunter C. Koch
Alyona Kondratyeva
Petro Kovaliv
Jonathan Koven
Ryan Thomas LaBee
Andrew Lafleche
Matthew Lane
Aaron Laughlin
Keon Lee
Jamie Leondaris
Todd Lewis
James M. Lindsay
Susie Little
Sara Long
LindaAnn LoSchiavo
Paul Luikart
Simina Lungu
Kim Malinowski
Davey Maloney
Laura Manuelidis
Eric McLaughlin
Laura McPherson
Hannah Melin
Skyler Melnick
Jack Miller
Zach Murphy
Kamran Muthleb
Paula Reed Nancarrow
Martina R. Newberry
Emily Newsome
Barbra Nightingale
Anna Novikova
Oleg Olizev
Josiah Olson
Vincent Oppedisano
Jaime Paniagua
Geena Papini
Rachel Anne Parsons
Kelly Pavelich
Elizabeth Paxson
Kristopher Pendleton
Simon Perchik
Barton Drew Perkins
W. C. Perry
Joseph Pete

Laura L. Petersen
Christina E. Petrides
Thomas Piekarski
Amanda Postman
John Pula
Richard Risemberg
Frank Rivera
Shannon Roberts
Joshua Robinson
Radoslav Rochallyi
Frank Roger
Brian Rosten
Rachel Sandell
Kamil Sariyev
Beatriz Seelaender
Margarita Serafimova
Evan James Sheldon
G.T. Shepherd
Kelli Simpson
Vladimir Slovesnyy
Paul Smith
Julia Solomakha
Alex Stearns
Michael Stein
J. J. Steinfeld
Travis Stephens
Emily Stevens
Liza Sofia
Gordon Stumpo
Patrick ten Brink
Simon Tertychniy
Steven Thomas
Caryl Gobin Ulrich
Rebekah VanDyk
Robin Vigfusson
Eugene Voron
Tiffany Washington
Jason Wallace
Carla Ward
Kim Welliver
Phil Wexler
Jack Wildern
Sybil Wilen
Christopher Williams
Lucky Williams
Erin Wilson
Cassondra Windwalker
Mariah Woodland
Ian Woollen
R.S. Wren
Ben Wrixon
Igor V. Zaitsev
Ann Zhang

The Hazardous Life

Philip Gambone

For the past several years, the Academy had not offered a fourth year of French. Three years of a foreign language were required for graduation, and that's as far as most of the students wanted to go. The one or two who occasionally opted for a fourth year were allowed to take an evening course at the Extension School down in Cambridge, for which the Academy gave them credit.

What a pity to send the students elsewhere, Mason Chastain always thought. As the Academy's senior French teacher, he knew these kids so well, knew what they needed, not only with regard to their studies but also in terms of their emotional growth. Their *spiritual* growth, he was tempted to say though he suspected that sounded old-fashioned. As so often, his favorite poet, Rimbaud, had expressed it perfectly: "I would have liked to show children these sunfish, the fish of gold, the singing fish on the blue tide." Mason doubted that the students the Academy sent to the Extension School would be shown those golden, singing fish. They'd be treated like mere adult learners rather than the intense, eager, romantic young people they were.

Then, in the final year of his forty-three-year career, a surprise occurred. Six students, the minimum needed to justify offering the class at the Academy, signed up for French IV, and the dean of studies asked Mason if he would teach the course. It would mean, he said, that Mason would have to give up one of his sections of second-year in order to teach the seniors. Not a fan of the dean, Mason said he'd need a few days to think about it. *Let him sweat it out,* Mason thought. But when he drove home that afternoon, he was already putting together a reading list. The blue tide was swelling.

* * *

As he circled the Back Bay looking for a parking spot, Mason knew it was petty to keep the dean in suspense, but there was something about Tony Krikorian that just rubbed him the wrong way. From the moment, six years ago, that Krikorian arrived as the new dean of studies, he had grated on Mason. It wasn't any one thing, but the whole package: Krikorian's youth (he was thirty-five), his good looks, his privileged Ivy-League education. The guy wore his lucky breaks — good genes, good breeding, good schools — with irritating self-assurance. He had an easy way with the kids, an easy way with the faculty. Mason had turned sixty that year. Krikorian's arrival had put him on guard.

The *coup de grâce* came three years ago when Krikorian, who was straight, volunteered to be the faculty advisor to the Gay-Straight Alliance. The previous faculty advisor had moved to Seattle with her wife and Krikorian stepped in to fill the vacancy. In another one of his countless irritating moves, he renamed the club the LGBTQIA+ Discussion Group.

The damn know-it-all, Mason thought as he circled the blocks around Commonwealth Avenue, looking for a parking space. Krikorian prided himself on being so *au courant*, so right-up-to-the-minute on all the latest, politically-correct views. Fifty years ago, when he, Mason, was in high school, it was just gays and straights — simple as that — with an occasional nod to the bisexuals, who no one really believed were bisexual at all. Now... my God, being gay was as humdrum as coq au vin. LGBTQIA+ indeed!

It was the middle of April and the magnolias on the sunny side of Commonwealth Avenue were in glorious full bloom. If the weather held, these blowzy, delicate pink blossoms would be resplendent for a week or so. Every year since he and Mary had lived in the Back Bay, Mason looked forward to the appearance of the magnolias. And it saddened him to contemplate how soon they would disappear. Recently, he had been feeling the poignancy of disappearing things ever more acutely.

There were no parking spaces on Commonwealth. He turned left on Fairfield — none there either — and then right onto Marlborough. His daily circle around the neighborhood in search of a place to park. Every year it got worse.

Before Krikorian had taken over the Gay-Straight Alliance, the Academy's headmaster had approached Mason about assuming the role of faculty advisor. After all, the headmaster said, Mason was a senior member of the faculty, had relatively small numbers of students, and had in the past led other clubs — French Club, Opera Club, the Spring Trip to Europe. Besides, the only gay member of the faculty now, Frank Fidby, the obvious candidate, was already teaching an extra section of chemistry and had no time. The headmaster thought that since it was a Gay-*Straight* Alliance, the group should occasionally be advised by a straight "ally."

How extraordinary, Mason thought. The Academy had certainly changed since the day when he first arrived, a young French teacher right out of the University of New Hampshire. Forty-three years ago, there had been no Gay-Straight Alliance. There had certainly been no teachers who would have declared themselves gay or lesbian. But now, everyone wanted to get in on the act. The woman who had previously run the GSA had even invited her students to her wedding when she married her wife. And Frank Fidby always brought his husband to soccer games and dances, when it was his turn to chaperone.

Even more remarkable, *students* at the Academy were now openly identifying themselves as gay and lesbian. And, it seemed, as every other variation along that rainbow spectrum — bisexual, transgender, nonbinary, gender-fluid, genderqueer. The categories bewildered Mason. He suspected that many of them, certainly the younger students, weren't even sexually active. The labels they gave themselves described what were still, he assumed, just abstract concepts for them, hardly lived experiences.

There were no spaces on Marlborough Street either. Mason circled the block again.

He thought back to his own teenage years. In the eighth grade, his best friend had been a boy named Gordie Henderson, whose hobby was photography. One day, Gordie gave Mason a tour of his basement darkroom: the enlarger, the developing trays, the dim, film-safe red lightbulb. Then he pulled out his collection of photo magazines. Leafing through them under that dim red light, Gordie pointed out the various articles, which were full of technical information on things like lenses, composition, film speeds. Each issue always included a suite of art photographs. Mason remembered one such spread in particular: it featured a wholesome, rosy-cheeked young woman kneeling in an outdoor setting. Her arms were raised above her head in order to keep a wide-brimmed hat (the only article of clothing she wore) from blowing off in the wind, a pose that thrust out her ample breasts in fulsome, robust vitality.

Gordie told Mason that these were "artistic" shots, taken by a highly regarded professional photographer, but the next time they got together — it was always on Tuesday afternoons after Confraternity of Christian Doctrine classes — Gordie started rubbing his crotch, exclaiming how much the girls in these beefcake spreads turned him on.

"Yeah," Mason agreed, wanting desperately to feel what Gordie was feeling.

For the rest of the winter of their eighth-grade year, he and Gordie spent each Tuesday afternoon in the darkroom masturbating to the magazines. Mason's eyes always strayed from the photographs to Gordie's cock, ready at a moment's notice to shift back to the photo spread in case Gordie noticed that his friend's attention had drifted. Mason liked the tight quarters of the darkroom, which meant that his body — his arms and hips — often touched Gordie's body while the two of them indulged in their separate bouts of self-pleasuring.

The car behind him honked. Mason looked up and saw that the stoplight was green. He turned onto Newbury Street. A block down, he spotted a parking space, pulled up, and eased into it. A lucky break on a Friday afternoon. And now the car could stay there all weekend without his having to move it. Unbuckling the seatbelt, he grabbed his briefcase and headed off to the little market down the block. The street was crowded with end-of-the-week shoppers and café patrons.

And, for an hour, I fell into the hubbub of a Baghdad street.

He'd been reading Rimbaud again, fiddling in his spare time with translations that he hoped would capture some of the astounding lyricism of that boy genius. The older he got, the more Mason found himself drawn to Rimbaud, to the beauty of his words, the outrageousness of his vision, a wild but perfect harmony. How astonishing that Rimbaud had produced most of his greatest work when he was still a teenager. Younger even than the seniors he would teach next year!

The weather was warm enough that a few guys — Back Bay gym rats

— were jogging down the street, their lean, beautiful bodies another declaration, like the magnolias, that the dash and brio of springtime had returned. *Ah, yes*, Mason thought, *buttoned-up Boston was throwing off its winter tweeds. Let the hubbub begin!*

By May of that eighth-grade year, Mason was in love with Gordie. He loved the intimate playfulness of their darkroom antics, the physical closeness, Gordie's happy-go-lucky attitude toward sex. He tried to imagine more with Gordie — what would that be? Maybe they'd go on vacations together, just the two of them, without their parents. Or end up roommates at the same college. As he and Gordie wacked off in the darkroom, Mason imagined an entire life with his friend. Then one day, watching Gordie panting in pre-climax excitement, Mason leaned over and tried to plant a kiss on Gordie's cheek. Gordie recoiled. "Fuck, man, what are you doing?" he barked. "Gross!" Mason was never invited back again.

* * *

The little Newbury Street market was crowded. Everyone there seemed to have the same idea on this beautiful springtime afternoon: prepare a nice meal, drink some wine, be with the ones you loved. Mason recognized at least one gay couple whom he often saw at the market. One was holding the grocery basket while the other picked items off the shelves — fresh pasta, a couple of artichokes, a quart of strawberries. Mason wondered what it would be like to feed a strawberry to another man, holding it to his lips, feeling his tongue touching his fingers.

The fall he entered high school, he and Gordie were blessedly not in the same classes. From the sidelines, Mason watched Gordie become quite the ladies' man, while he, in turn, buried himself, and his shame, in his studies. French — so foreign, so romantic, so beautiful — became his favorite subject. More than that, it became his refuge. He managed to stop mooning over Gordie, though he could not help having secret crushes on other boys, none of which he dared to act on. Senior year, his French teacher assigned them Gide's *Symphonie pastorale.* The other students in the class weren't as proficient as Mason, and they labored over the book for months. Mason was bored out of his mind — with the story, with the pace, with their teacher's tedious droning on and on. This story of a secret, unrequited heterosexual love was not the story he needed to read.

That final year of high school French had been so bad that Mason almost didn't take another French course when he got to college. But his advisor at the University of New Hampshire told him his French preparation had been so strong — and his Achievement Test so high — that he could pass into upper-level courses if he wanted to. Mason thought he'd give it a try. The poetry course he took turned out to be excellent. As did the other French course he took that year, "Proust and His World." By June, he'd declared himself a French major. It was the first time in his life that he was absolutely sure he'd made the right choice.

He was less sanguine about his decision to join a fraternity, but fraternities were the way to go back then and so he did it. At his first boozy frat party, Mason got drunk and then never again. He was afraid of what he might do if he let his guard down. At other parties, when his fraternity brothers told jokes about fags and homos, he responded with fainthearted smiles. The guys began to see him as the goody two-shoes of their house. They nicknamed him Chastity Chastain. "Chastity, isn't it about time you got banged in Boston?" they teased. By junior year, Mason was secretly wishing he could drop out of the fraternity. And then he met Mary.

She was five years older than he, a graduate student and teaching fellow in the course he took that year in abnormal psychology. Often after class, he'd linger to ask her questions. At first, she gave him only a minute or two of her time before she went off to do more research at the library. But one day, she invited him to join her for coffee. With guarded casualness, Mason brought up that week's topic: the recent decision by the American Psychiatric Association to depathologize homosexuality. With equally guarded casualness, Mary acknowledged that it was a "landmark readjustment," one that would have profound consequences for how *gay* people — he had already noticed how she preferred that word over "homosexual" — how gay people would think about themselves from now on. "Lesbians, too," she added. He remembered how she had looked down at her coffee cup and then back up at him, fishing for a reaction.

The next Saturday, they went to the White Mountains with the hiking club. It turned out that Mary was an outdoor enthusiast. Though she was a few inches shorter than he, Mary had a rugged, boyishly-athletic body, and could hike at quite the clip. Mason had never been on a hike before, and had a hard time keeping up with her, but he enjoyed talking to Mary about psychology and French and their similar blue-collar backgrounds. When the weather got too cold for hikes, they did other things together — concerts, plays, trips into Boston for the museums (his choices); basketball games, skiing, bird watching (her choices).

One day — it was the spring semester and she was no longer his teacher — Mary told him her story: married at twenty-one, a child (now three years old), and a divorce about to be finalized. "I'm not sure there was ever much of a spark there," she told Mason. "Bob and I were just two people, much too young to get married, who happened to share a passion for psychology. Not enough reason to keep a marriage alive."

"What do you think *does* keep a marriage alive?" he asked.

She gave him another one of her sober, direct looks. "Well, for starters, the courage to make a go of it together, I'd say. I think in the end, Bob and I just couldn't muster that kind of courage."

Those sounded like such beautiful words — courage, making a go of it. He thought about what it would be like to share a long life with another person: keeping a house, raising a child, working side-by-side at the dining room table after supper, bandying ideas back and forth, taking trips to Europe. When he tried to imagine sex with Mary, he thought he could give that a try, too. Two weeks later, they slept together. He'd forgotten to bring a condom and Mary said she was not on the pill. So they just slept together, and this seemed fine with both of them.

"I think I'm a lesbian," she told him halfway through that night.

"I think I'm a gay man," he told her. Though tenuous, it was the first declaration of his sexuality he had ever made to anyone.

In the market's wine section, Mason picked up two bottles, a Merlot for himself, a Chardonnay for Mary, her favorite. Then he put the red back on the shelf. Otherwise, he knew he'd drink the entire bottle over the course of the evening, and probably finish Mary's bottle of white. He was doing that a lot lately. He thought he should probably slow down.

A month after he graduated — by then Mary's divorce had been finalized — they got married. It was a crazy decision, and yet it wasn't. He couldn't imagine another person who would ever know him — and *accept* him — as well as Mary did. They had grown fond of each other, enough to embark on an outwardly conventional partnership in a quietly unconventional way. Mary said that they were forging "a common front" against everything they hated — shame, theories of abnormality, the frat boys. Remarkably, they had been making a go of it together ever since. Mason's fiftieth high school reunion was coming up next year. He wondered if Gordie would be there and what he would say when Mason showed up with a wife.

Just before he got into the checkout line, he added a bouquet of tulips and a quart of strawberries to his basket.

* * *

The building where he and Mary owned a condo was an elegant, late-nineteenth-century townhouse that had been broken up into apartments years ago, one of the first of these old Commonwealth Avenue mansions to go condo. He and Mary had lived in the Back Bay their entire married life, first in a cheap one-bedroom rental on Hereford Street, later in a nicer apartment on Beacon Street, and now, for the past thirty-three years, in this building, which the developers had christened "The Standish," a name that was supposed to connote, he guessed, Yankee history, decorum, and sober-ness. They purchased their unit with a down payment from Mary's parents. In those early days, three bedrooms were still affordable. One bedroom was theirs, another for the days when Mary's son Ben was with them, and the third they converted into an office for her therapy practice. Ben's bedroom was now Mason's study.

He took the elevator up to their floor and let himself in. Mary was at the kitchen table, working at her laptop.

"I hope you got outside today," Mason said. "It's positively glorious out there."

Mary looked up, peering over her half-frame reading glasses, and smiled. "I managed to get in a walk between patients earlier this afternoon." As Mason began to unpack his shopping bag, she noticed the flowers and berries. "How lovely!"

"A little something to celebrate the season. The strawberries are from California, of course, but... well, I'm feeling festive." When Mary sent him a quizzical look, he explained: "Krikorian wants me to teach French IV next year." He went to the sink, turned on the tap and began to rinse the berries. "I told him I'd think about it."

"But you will, won't you?"

As the strawberries we rinsing, he put the tulips in a vase and filled it with water.

"Mason, you've wanted to teach that course for years," Mary continued, "and next year... well, it would be a lovely swansong."

"Dear me, 'swansong.' Sounds like I'm dying."

"Oh, stop!" she chided, taking the vase of tulips from his hands and setting it on the table.

Mason laughed — more to reassure her than because he saw the humor in her remark. He dumped the strawberries into a bowl, opened a kitchen drawer, and pulled out a corkscrew. "Want a glass?"

Mary glanced up at the kitchen clock. "A small one, Mason. I have a patient coming at five."

He opened the Chardonnay and poured glasses for both of them before sitting down across from her. They clinked.

"Simone Dugied was the last one to teach the fourth-year course. Which is probably why none of the seniors in recent years have signed up." He took a sip of the wine. It was cold and delicious. "Poor old gal. Simone stayed on at the Academy way past her prime. Her fourth-year course was a snoozer."

Mason took a strawberry from the bowl and brought it to Mary's lips. She pulled back and took it from his fingers.

"Mason, being a teacher at the Academy was Simone's whole identity." She bit into the strawberry. "She loved the school as much as you do. I suspect that staying on as long as she did kept Simone young."

"Ah, but there's the rub. Is that enough of a reason to keep teaching? I mean, it's supposed to be about the kids — right? I don't think it's enough of a reason to stay in the classroom just because it 'keeps you young.'"

"So is that why you're retiring next year? You think you're getting stale?"

He swirled his glass. "There are days when I do."

"And on the other days?"

He moved his attention from the glass to his wife. She was seventy-two and still going strong. Only last month, Mary had announced that she planned to keep her practice open until she was at least seventy-five.

"On other days, I think I still have it." He smiled at her. "That's why this chance to teach the French IV kids really intrigues me. I want to" — he chuckled — "I want to get revenge on the Madame Dugieds of the world! The ones who *should* have retired and didn't."

"Dear me, Mason. The poor woman."

He picked a strawberry out of the bowl, bit into it. The juice ran down his chin. Mary picked a napkin from the napkin holder on the table and patted his chin dry.

"Do you think you might stay beyond next year?" she asked.

"No, I don't think so."

"You don't sound convinced."

"Convince me," he said.

It was Mary's turn to chuckle.

Convince me was their private joke. Five years into their marriage, Mason had begun having second thoughts. By then, both he and Mary were seeing other people: a casual love affair on Mary's part with a woman several years older than she; a more unsettling affair on his part with a twenty-one-year-old college senior. "Convince me, Mary," he had appealed to her one night, "convince me why we should stay together. I love you, but this is driving me crazy. I think I love Cameron, too."

That's when she'd said it: "Let's never ask each other that, for one of us to convince the other. That's not a responsibility I'll accept." She'd gone on to say that *she* was convinced that their marriage was the one she wanted. "What's going on between me and Rachel, or you and Cameron, has nothing to do with our *marriage*. But I don't want to be put in the position of having to convince you of that. Only you can decide whether you want this marriage. I can only tell you that I do."

In the years since, they'd each had other affairs. Mary always let her lovers know, from the start, that she was committed to her marriage; there was no possibility, she told these women, of their ever becoming a couple. Her husband and her son came first.

When he and Cameron broke it off — Mason using the same dictum:

his wife and son came first — he thought that maybe he'd gotten it, whatever "it" was, out of his system. But about a year later, he found he couldn't beat down his curiosity: what might some other man offer him that Cameron had not, that domestic life was not?

One afternoon, he stopped in at a gay bar near the Public Library for a cocktail before he went home. Just a drink, he told himself, nothing more. On his third visit there, he met Bill. Bill lasted about as long as Cameron, half a year. "I just don't want to be your mistress," he told Mason. "I understand," Mason said, "but my wife and son come first."

The third and last affair was with a guy named Loring, who was a civil rights lawyer. Loring said he was happy just to be Mason's occasional thing — he respected that Mason's family was important. But a year into their "arrangement," Loring told Mason he had tested positive for HIV. The news scared the hell out of Mason. Though they had been practicing safe sex, he was terrified he might bring something home to Mary. That was the year he and Mary bought their place on Commonwealth Avenue. Ben was sixteen, a junior at the Academy. Mason decided that his life was rich enough without the complications that Loring, or any other guy, brought into the equation. Still, he and Loring remained friends — dinner buddies on evenings when Mary was out with her bowling league, later a meals-on-wheels deliverer when Loring was too sick to take care of himself. When Loring died, he and Mary both attended the memorial service.

Mary picked another strawberry out of the bowl. "You don't *have* to retire, you know."

"I know," he agreed. "Sometimes it feels as if I've only made that decision because I think I'm supposed to make it." She waited for him to go on. "I've thought about delaying taking social security and continuing at the Academy a few more years." She waited again. "Mary, I just don't want to become another Simone Dugied!"

There, he'd said it, he'd confessed his deepest fear. He did not want to watch himself become a washed-up, has-been teacher. Teaching had been his whole life. What else did he have to show for himself? Plenty, he guessed: his forty-four-year marriage to this good woman, his stepson Ben, and now his two grandsons. Those were things to feel proud of, too. But in so many other ways — his desire to write poetry, his dream that they would one day own a house in France, those silly affairs and infatuations that had gone nowhere — there was so much... what should he call it? *unfulfillment* in his life. Years ago, he had stopped his occasional pop-ins at one of the local gay bars. That was another thing to feel good about, too, though Mason sometimes wondered if his withdrawal from gay flirtation had more to do with the fact that gay bars in Boston were closing left and right.

"Mason, you could never become another Simone Dugied," Mary said affectionately. "Krikorian would never have asked you to teach the course if he had thought that."

He leaned across the table and kissed her cheek. "You're my greatest fan."

"Always have been, Mason."

They never had kids. Mary's son, Ben, whose custody she had shared with the boy's father, until he died of cancer, was the only child in their lives. Now forty-eight, Ben was a former rock guitarist who had become a successful agent for rock bands. Married at twenty-five, he'd given them two grandsons, who were — my God, the years were flying by! — nineteen and twenty-one this year. Becoming a grandfather — Boppy, the boys still called him — was another reason that Mason's passion for outside affairs had slackened. It just didn't square in his mind: the occasional Friday night forays into gay bars followed by the two of them babysitting the boys on Saturdays. Rimbaud had a phrase for the way that made him feel: "with this throat wrapped in a necktie of shame."

He poured himself more Chardonnay and then went to add more to Mary's glass. She held her hand over the rim.

"My patient's coming."

He smiled affectionately at her. "We are both so levelheaded."

"Forty-four years of levelheadedness next month," she said. "*Imagine ça!*"

* * *

At the end of the school year, Tony Krikorian called Mason into his office to finalize his teaching schedule for next year.

"Madame Dugied was the last one to teach the fourth-year class," he said, as if Mason didn't know this already. "We wrote to her — you know she's living on Cape Cod now—"

"Yes, the *Cape*," Mason interrupted. It irked him how Krikorian, who'd grown up in Fresno, California, had never learned the Boston way of referring to Cape Cod.

"She dug up her old syllabus," Krikorian continued, clueless that he'd been corrected. He handed Mason a sheet of paper on which was mimeographed a list of the fourth-year books. Mason glanced at it. Just as he suspected: a dull, unimaginative syllabus. An old lady's syllabus. My God, they were supposed to start with the *Symphonie pastorale!*

"And this," Krikorian said, handing him another sheet, is your class list. "Quite an impressive crew, I'd say."

Mason read the names. He'd taught all six of them back when they were sophomores: Sabrina Belknap, a good student and crack field hockey player; the twins Mary-Margaret and Margaret-Mary Donohue; another girl Chenguang Lee, whose American name was Dawn; and two boys, Nathan Coverdale, the least successful of the six back in his sophomore year, and — Mason tried to disguise his delight — Duncan Dietrich, one of the sharpest students at the Academy.

"Looks like a good group," he told Krikorian, handing back the list. "Though I'm surprised Nathan Coverdale signed up. He barely passed French II."

Krikorian smiled. "Sabrina Belknap," he said. "The two of them are an item. At least for now. I guess we'll see how things pan out over the summer."

"You'd be okay with my changing the reading list a bit?" Mason asked, irritated that Krikorian even knew the amatory background of the students. "I might want to make some tweaks." He intended to whether or not Krikorian gave the nod.

"No problem," Krikorian told him with that hang-loose amiability of his.

"*Eh bien, je vous souhaite d'agréables vacances d'été,*" Mason said, enjoying every delicious second of Krikorian's incomprehension.

* * *

All summer, Mason read. And all summer he cut books from Simone Dugied's syllabus, adding his own choices. The short story unit was easy — so many great ones to choose from. As for the novel, well, certainly not the *Symphonie pastorale.* Maybe Zola's *Nuits des Temps.* Or something by Balzac or Camus. For fun, during the doldrums of winter, he thought Sempé's Petit Nicolas book might work or Queneau's *Exercices de Style.* Then there was the question of poetry. Again, a world of choices. He had to admit that some of the poems on Simone's list weren't so bad, though she hadn't included a single poem by Rimbaud. Well, the poetry unit fell in the spring. He'd decide later, based on how the class was going.

At the beginning of August, he and Mary took their annual two-week vacation to Wellfleet. It was at the outer end of the Cape, an hour's drive from where Simone Dugied and her husband had retired. The thought occurred to him that he should drop in to see her and discuss the course. Just as quickly, he abandoned that idea. But among the books he packed to read, he threw in the *Symphonie pastorale.* He thought he should at least read it again before he officially dropped it from the reading list. *Maybe,* he thought, *he'd dump the thing on Simone's front lawn on his way home at the end of the summer.*

Each morning after breakfast, he and Mary went for a swim, then spent the rest of the time before lunch reading, he his French books, Mary her English mystery novels. Afternoons they went to the beach again or took walks or did some bird watching. In the evening, after dinner, they watched movies, played Scrabble, read some more. Mary's French was not nearly as good as Mason's, but a few days into the vacation, she picked up the Gide when Mason wasn't reading it and started making her way through the first few pages. The next morning, she went to the Wellfleet Public Library and took out a copy of *The Pastoral Symphony* in English.

On the last night of their vacation, one of Mary's friends came over for dinner. Priscilla was another therapist. She and Mary had had an affair back when they were in their fifties, but now they were just friends. Every summer Priscilla rented the house next to theirs. Mason envied how these two women had remained close over the years.

Priscilla arrived with a potato salad and a bottle of Chardonnay.

"I would have made dessert," she told them, "but I spent the day in Provincetown." She joined Mary at the kitchen table. "It's Carnival Week." She raised her eyes in mock bewilderment. "Oh, those boys."

Mason was at the stove working on a bouillabaisse, wondering what in the world they'd do with Priscilla's potato salad, and delighted she hadn't brought dessert. Priscilla was a terrible cook. He turned and smiled.

"Those boys, indeed."

The last time he'd been in Provincetown, the last time he'd seen Carnival, was fifteen years ago.

After dinner and dessert — Mason had made a tarte Tatin — Mary and Priscilla did the dishes. This was the unerring rule they'd followed their entire married life: whoever cooked left the dishes for the other. Mason counted it a good deal since he hated doing dishes and loved to cook. He left the ladies at the kitchen sink and went to the living room, where, under the autumnal glow of a reading lamp, he made his way through the final pages of the *Symphonie pastorale*. He was beside himself with impatience, boredom, and outright animosity. He'd never liked the novel, which he considered a piece of namby-pamby mushiness, and reading it again only confirmed his distaste. The symbolism of the physically blind girl and the morally blind pastor — it was trite and obvious.

"Done!" he announced, snapping the book shut. "I don't think I could have stood one more page."

He heard Mary explaining to Priscilla what he was talking about.

"I don't know why he bothered to read it again," she told her friend.

He heaved himself up from the chair and returned to the kitchen.

"Academic integrity," he explained. "Due diligence. I was hoping I'd find something in it that would convince me to change my mind."

"Did you?" Priscilla asked.

"Not a thing! Don't get me wrong. Gide's a beautiful writer, a great writer, and his basic message here — he brandished the book in front of her — it's one I can buy into."

"What's that?" Priscilla asked.

Mason opened the book, flipped through a few pages, and read to them: "*Le mal n'est jamais dans l'amour.* There's never anything wrong with love."

"You think that's true?" Priscilla asked. "*Never?*"

"Well, in the context of the passage, Gide intends it somewhat ironically. The blind girl — her name is Gertrude — has just told the Pastor she loves him. It's an innocent remark. She wouldn't say that, she tells him, if he were not married. 'So, why shouldn't we love each other?' she asks. Of course, the Pastor is burning with undisclosed passion for her."

"And she doesn't know that?" Priscilla asked.

"No, not until the very end when... Do you want to know how it ends?"

"You've piqued my curiosity," Priscilla told him. "So, no, don't tell me. I just might read it myself."

Mason shook his head in exasperation. "How such a great writer — and a homosexual, to boot! — how he could have written this... this..."

Priscilla looked at Mary. Mason knew that back when they'd had their affair, Mary had told Priscilla that her husband was gay.

(*And what did she say,* he'd later asked Mary. *She said she thought we were very modern,* Mary told him. *Is that the word for us?* Mason asked. *Mod-*

ern? Mary had smiled. *I told her we were just very us,* she said.)

"Why do you think Simone had *The Pastoral Symphony* on her list?" Mary asked. Her tone was the same one she used with her patients when she wanted to suggest to them the possibility of another point of view other than the one they were insisting upon.

"Well, I suppose because it's the right level of difficulty and the kind of story that appeals — or at least *used* to appeal — to impressionable teenagers."

"The love story, you mean?" Priscilla asked.

"The love *triangle*," Mason said, landing on the word with an emphasis he immediately regretted. He pretended to be interested in picking up a few crumbs from the half-eaten tarte, which was sitting on the kitchen counter. "The Pastor's *son* and Gertrude are in love."

"Well, that sounds interesting." Priscilla's laugh — deep, chesty, mannish — had always struck Mason as a dead giveaway that she was a lesbian.

Mary handed the last washed plate to Priscilla, who took it in her toweled hands, like a midwife swaddling a baby. Then she pulled the stopper from the drain and turned to Mason.

"I don't know, Mason, I think you're being a bit harsh. Granted, I didn't read it in French, but I liked it a lot. He's trying to get across that the only real sin is the one that tries to squash the happiness of another."

"That's beautiful," Priscilla said.

Mason was beginning to feel foolish. "It is," he conceded. "But Gide said it so much better in several other books."

"Then choose another of his books," Mary said. "It's your course now, Mason."

"Yeah, my swansong."

* * *

On the Tuesday after Labor Day, Mason met his French IV class for the first time. Because the class was so small, it was held not in Mason's regular classroom but in the Hitchcock Seminar Room, a special privilege for seniors. This seminar room, outfitted with a large oval table and Windsor armchairs, had once been the former library of Hitchcock House, a fieldstone mansion located on the far side of the Academy's soccer fields. Hitchcock House was atypical of domestic architecture in this part of Massachusetts, but typical, Mason guessed, of the quirky family who had built it in the twenties of the last century and who, upon the death of old Mrs. Hitchcock, had bequeathed the mansion and an additional twenty acres of playing fields to the school.

Mason loved the seminar room. It represented so much of what he stood for as a teacher: a sun-filled, scholarly retreat from the noisy adolescent bustle in the main school building. He loved the relaxed give-and-take of discussions around that splendid oval table rather than the regimentation of the hideous stainless-steel-and-plastic desk-chair setups in the regular classrooms. He loved the sheer joy of the collegial intimacy he could create here.

He got to the seminar room early, took his place at the head of the table, and arranged his books and papers, including packets of a handout that he had photocopied for each student. *My final year*, he thought. *Nail it.* As the six students drifted in, he greeted each one warmly. He still remembered the French names he'd given them during their sophomore year: the twins, who arrived together, were Marie-Margaret and Margaret-Marie, though he'd forgotten how to tell them apart. Next to enter were Sabrina and Chenguang.

"*Bonjour, Sabine et Aurore!*"

"*Bonjour, Monsieur Chastain*," they responded in unison.

Nathan was next. Two years ago, he'd rejected the French name — Nathaniel — that Mason had given him and chosen Claude, after his favorite French composer, Claude Debussy. Nathan was a pianist, a far better pianist than a French student.

Last to arrive was Duncan Dietrich, whom Mason had christened Dorian.

"It's lovely to see you all again," he told them, opting for user-friendly English.

All six assured him it was good to see him, too. They looked refreshed and eager, ready to tackle the challenges of their senior year.

But what was this, Mason thought, as his attention went to the book each of them had brought to class. To his consternation, they had shown up with copies of the *Symphonie pastorale*. After all the work he'd put in that summer to create a new syllabus, he had forgotten to send the revised list to Krikorian, and so the dean had mailed the students Simone Dugied's old syllabus.

"*Eh bien, mes élèves.*" He had always scrupulously avoided calling them by the more motherly, infantilizing *mes enfants,* which is how Simone Dugied had addressed her students. "I see you have all dutifully brought in *La Symphonie pastorale.*"

"Our brother read it when he took this course," one of the Donohue twins said. "Would it be okay if I used his copy? It's got his notes in it."

"It would indeed be okay... *if* we were reading it this year."

A concerned look darkened the face of the twin — he guessed it was Marie-Margaret, who had always been the more fretful of the two.

"We're not?"

Mason took in a deep breath. He had to tread tactfully here. "The *Symphonie pastorale* many say is one of Gide's finest works. However, I regret to say that I do not share that opinion. Gide wrote several far greater books." He paused again, surveying the sextet of students assembled around the seminar table. He knew that, at the moment, he had their complete trust, but he was about to drop a bombshell. "In fact," he continued, "*je déteste ce roman.*" There, he'd thrown down the gauntlet. "I think it's rather... well, a piece of sentimental hogwash."

He saw Sabine's eyes open wide. The twins tilted their heads together and confabbed in whispers.

"Our brother loved it," one of them declared.

"I'm glad he did," Mason said, "and I hope you'll learn to love the Gide that I'll be teaching this semester." He began distributing packets of photocopied material that, luckily, he had prepared and brought to class. "So, we are *indeed* going to start with Monsieur Gide. But a very different Gide.

These excerpts are from his first published work. He was twenty-one when he wrote it. Only three years older than you."

"I'm seventeen," Sabine said.

"Me, too," Aurore added.

"Okay, so *four* years older," Mason said, trying to strike a balance, which he hoped the two girls would detect, between amusement and annoyance. He'd intended to stress just how very young Gide had been when he brought out his first book, but Mason now realized that to these teenagers twenty-one was still light years away.

Aurore raised her hand, her head buried in the handout, already reading.

"No need to raise your hands this year," Mason announced to them all. "You're a small class and I want to run it like a seminar. Aurore, *as-tu une question?*"

"So, what is this? It looks like a diary."

"Precisely. These are passages from a book called *Les Cahiers d'André Walter. The Notebooks of André Walter.* André Walter was a fictitious character, but Gide used that character as a vehicle to present his own thoughts. He was trying to figure out who he was." He paused and looked at them. "It's his early psychological self-portrait. He wanted to discover what made him tick." He had their attention now, most of them anyway. Nathan was lost in staring at Sabrina. As for the Donohue twins, he wondered if he had laid to rest their brother's buildup of the *Symphonie pastorale.* He continued with his little promo spiel:

"Gide was an advocate for undaunted living, *la vie intense,* he called it. He said that everything happens deep in the soul. The polite surface we present to the world... well, it's a lie. We suffer when we're unable to reveal our true selves." He saw that Nathan was now whispering to Sabrina. "Do you have something to share with the class, Claude?"

Nathan hurriedly broke off. "No, sir."

"Well, then. Pay attention. Today we are discussing literature, not the senior prom." Sabrina blushed; Aurore giggled. "So, back to Gide. Dorian, the first passage, if you please." Mason wanted to start off without any stumbling over words or syntax. He knew Dorian was his man.

"*L'air est si radieux ce matin...*"

Dorian's accent was perfect. Mason listened with pleasure as the boy continued. When Dorian got to the end of the excerpt, Mason asked Chenguang to translate.

"This morning the air is so... radiant?" she asked.

"*C'est exact.* Radiant, bright, clear."

"So clear this morning that... *malgré moi,* in spite of myself, my soul hopes."

"*Très bien.* Continue please, Marie-Margaret."

"And sings, and adores with a desire for prayers."

"A desire for prayers," Mason repeated. "But how would we say that in English. Gide said it in his idiom; what would be ours? His soul is so elated by the radiant day that it sings and adores..."

"With a desire to pray... to God?" she asked timidly.

"I don't see God in that sentence, mademoiselle."

Mary-Margaret's sister came to the rescue: "Well, who else would the soul be praying to?"

"Ah, a profound question, my dear. So: *avec un désir de prières.* Anyone else want to hazard a guess?"

"A longing to pray?" Duncan ventured. "A longing to cry out?"

"Indeed." Mason refrained from smiling too adoringly at Duncan, lest it become obvious who his favorite one was already. The other night, he'd been finishing up a translation of another Rimbaud poem. It contained the phrase *pubescence d'or* — golden puberty. It was hard not to think of Duncan as enjoying that kind of radiant adolescence.

"Gide once said that everything happens deep in the soul. What do you suppose he meant by that?" Mason had thrown the question out to anyone, but he now addressed one of the twins directly. "Margaret-Marie? *Que penses-tu?*"

"I think he means that God lives deep in our souls.

Duncan began to shake his head.

"Dorian? You disagree?"

"Gide was an atheist."

"Well, yes and no. He was raised in a strict Protestant family and, at least during his early life, struggled to live by Christian values. But, yes, he was a champion of what he called 'living mightily' — *vivre puissamment* — not letting himself be cowed, intimidated by life. *Que tout me soit une éducation.* 'Let everything be an education for me.' He believed that everything worth living for was worth going a little crazy for. Reason may keep us on the straight and narrow, but it makes the life of the soul *insupportable*, intolerable. He wanted to be open to all that life presented him; he wanted to be true to his own…" Mason paused, realizing he'd been addressing only Duncan and not the rest of the class. "True to his own nature," he told them all.

"He was a homosexual, right?" Duncan asked.

"And *where* did you learn that?" Mason asked.

"Wikipedia."

"Ah, Wikipedia," Mason declared. "Yes, Gide was…"

Marie-Margaret cut him short. "Gide was *gay?*"

"It's not the word he would have used," Mason told the class. "But yes. By the way, since we should be learning some new French vocabulary this year, does anyone know the modern French word for 'gay'?"

"*Gai,*" Duncan piped up, ever eager, in his charming way, to shine. "Also *homosexuel.* And I've also heard *pédé.*" Duncan was the student president of the Gay-Straight Alliance.

Mason raised his eyebrows. "Wikipedia has taught you a lot, *mon cher Dorian.*"

A look of pleasure and embarrassment bloomed on Duncan's face. "Actually, I learned that in the LGBTQIA+ Discussion Group. During orientation last week, Mr. Krikorian showed us a gay French film. It had subtitles. Not everyone in the Discussion Group takes French."

"I'm sure the LGB Etcetera greatly appreciates the linguistic advantage you bring to the club," Mason told him.

Everyone laughed. *Yes*, Mason thought, *I'm going to nail it this year.*

* * *

Over the next few weeks, things happened fast. Krikorian called Mason into his office to report that Mrs. Donohue had complained that the *Symphonie pastorale* had been taken off the French IV syllabus. Mason gave him the same pitch he'd given the kids: there were better works by Gide. This seemed to satisfy the dean, but two days later, Mason was called in again. There was another complaint: Mrs. Donohue had decided that *The Notebooks of André Walter* were... "Well, the word she used was degenerate," he told Mason.

"Oh, Christ, Tony! That's ridiculous."

"I know, I know," Krikorian assured him, but he sounded harried, caught between two competing concerns.

"Look," Mason said, "come sit in on the class, if you want. You'll see what horribly 'degenerate' things we're reading."

Krikorian said he would, but Mason could tell that observing the class was just one more task on the dean's already overburdened list of problems to solve. He actually began to feel a bit of sympathy for the guy.

Krikorian made his visitation a few days later. "Twenty minutes," he said, "that's all I'll need." Mason took pains to select an excerpt that he thought would perfectly show off the beauty of Gide's thinking and, at the same time, send a virtual barb into Mrs. Donohue's timid, bourgeois heart. When the class got to the stinger passage, he deliberately called on one of the Donohue twins to translate.

"Margaret-Marie?"

"Something about minds," she began.

"*Narrow* minds," Mason suggested, swallowing his irritation that she didn't know the word.

"Narrow minds, which think that, um, that theirs is the only truth. Truth is multiple, infinite, as diverse as there are, um..."

"As diverse as there are minds to think," Mason finished, now giving into his impatience. He glanced at Krikorian, who was standing in a corner, arms crossed. The expression on his face gave away nothing. "Truth is *multiple*, Gide says. What do you guys think of that?" His eyes scanned the six students around the oval table.

Margaret-Marie raised her hand: "My mother says that Gide..."

"I don't give a..." Mason caught himself. "Your mother isn't the one taking this course, my dear." He deliberately avoided looking at Krikorian.

No one spoke until Duncan said, "Monsieur, you said Gide wrote this when he was twenty-one. Did he know he was gay then? Because if he did, I see exactly why he'd say that truth is multiple."

"Go on," Mason coached.

"Well, gay people — I know Gide wouldn't have used that word — but gay people experience a whole different way of being in the world. I mean, their 'truth' is not the truth that straight people are handed — you know, the whole heteronormative script that says attraction to the opposite sex is the only way to be, that you have to get married and have two-point-five kids…"

"Gay people can get married!" Sabine protested.

"What's 'heteronormative'?" Nathan/Claude asked.

"Let Dorian finish," Mason told them.

"What I'm saying" — Duncan addressed Sabrina directly — "is that gay people have to figure it out for themselves, have to find out what's right for themselves apart from what society says is right. I *love* what Gide said: 'Truth is multiple'! That's awesome."

Mason let Duncan's words ripple through the seminar room, like the slow dying out of a pealing bell. He had not intended to push a gay agenda today, but there it was. He hoped it all hadn't been too much for Krikorian. When he looked up, Krikorian gave him a thumbs up.

But the next day, Krikorian called him back into the office. It was Mrs. Donohue again.

"She called me last night," the dean said. "She's complaining that you're turning the French IV seminar into a propaganda piece for the — to quote her — 'the homosexual agenda.'"

"I am *not* turning the French IV seminar into anything but what it's intended to be," Mason said, "the reinforcement and extension" — he held up one finger — "of the French studies they've done the past three years" — he held up a second finger — "studying some great literature" — a third finger went up — "and a preparation for the intellectual challenge they'll face in college. This class is not a catechism class, Tony. If Mrs. Donohue wants to keep her precious girls intellectually repressed, let her…"

"Mason," Krikorian interrupted, "she's already decided to pull the twins out. They're going to take French at the Extension School."

Mason stood there, shaking his head in disbelief.

"I feel sorry for the twins."

Krikorian nodded in agreement. "It was a good class I saw yesterday, Mason. Those girls will miss out on a valuable experience. They'll miss out on *you*. Anyway, you've got yourself a class of four now."

Mason left early that day. He was eager to tell Mary what had transpired. But when he let himself into the apartment, she wasn't there. A note on the kitchen table told him she'd gone for a walk along the Charles with Priscilla. *Gorgeous afternoon*, she'd written. *Won't be many of these days left.*

It was the third week in September. *Of course there would be more beautiful days*, Mason thought, *right through October.* The fact that Mary felt it necessary to justify her afternoon escape irked him. Two hours later, she called to say that Priscilla had invited her to stay for supper.

"Girl time," she explained.

"I need *wife* time," Mason said forlornly. He explained what had transpired that day. Mary offered appropriate consolation.

"You win some, you lose some, Mason," she told him. "If anything, this frees you up to make the seminar even more of what you dreamed it would be."

Mason chuckled. "What *did* I dream it would be?" At that moment, he couldn't put a word to what he'd been trying to accomplish. A protest, he guessed. But against whom? Simone Dugied was the obvious answer, but he knew he was railing against something much larger.

* * *

In the days after the departure of the Donohue twins, the two girls who remained in the class, Sabine and Aurore, were subdued. Mason worked extra hard to rekindle their enthusiasm. So did Nathan, who alternately flirted with each of them.

Happily, Mason did not need to work at all to maintain Duncan's scholastic enthusiasm. The boy couldn't get enough of Gide. He would stay after class to pursue an idea or ask Mason's advice on what to read next.

"I just learned this," he told Mason one day after class, "but I'm sure you already knew it, that he married his cousin. A *woman*."

"Yes," Mason said. "And it turned out not to be a happy marriage."

"I don't understand why — you know, if Gide was so unashamedly gay — why he did that."

"Oh, I suppose there are lots of explanations," Mason offered. "Social pressure mostly, don't you think?"

"My great uncle — my grandmother's brother? — he's gay, but when he was young, he married a woman. I guess *that* was social pressure." Mason tried not to look too interested. He'd never been comfortable when his students shared details about their families. "Then," Duncan continued, "when he was in his fifties, he finally came out. He's sixty-eight now. He's been with his boyfriend for eleven years."

"He has a boyfriend?" Mason asked. It was an idiotic question — Duncan had just told him so — but the question had popped out and there it was, like an admission that he was curious for more.

"Yeah, his boyfriend is, like, twelve years younger. My grandmother won't even talk to them, but my mom loves them. We go see them every Christmas."

"They live around here?"

"No, Los Angeles. Mark — that's my great uncle's boyfriend — he's a curator at one of the museums out there. Uncle Ralph's retired."

"So," Mason pursued, as delicately as possible, "are you" — a slight pause — "*out* to your great uncle?"

A smile blossomed on Duncan's face. "Totally. In fact, Uncle Mark and Uncle Ralph are the ones who coached me on how to come out to my parents."

"Duncan, that's *awesome*." Mason listened to himself using the vocabulary of his students' generation, something he'd avoided doing his entire teaching career. He wondered how much Duncan had figured out about his French teacher. Everyone knew that Monsieur Chastain was married, but he had never shied away from addressing issues of homosexuality when they came up in class. Sometimes, he'd even initiated those discussions. A sharp boy like Duncan... maybe he'd already figured out the situation. Then again, what exactly *was* the situation? Mason had been trying to figure that out all his life.

* * *

The surprises continued. By the end of October, Mary and Priscilla were seeing a lot of each other. *Too much of each other,* Mason thought. Tuesday nights had become their nights to have dinner together. And then there were long walks on Saturdays, Sunday afternoon trips to the Museum, the occasional afternoon coffee. He decided to ask Mary outright if they had resumed their affair.

"I mean, it would be okay with me if you were," he told Mary, "but I'd just like to know." The "okay" was tentative, a feeler he was casting out.

"Well, we aren't" Mary said. "Mason, Priscilla and I are both seventy-two. We each have a life that's working for us." She looked at him affectionately and smiled. "Working *very well.* And we're both quite aware of how unwise it would be to fall into a romance again."

"Sounds as if you've discussed this with her."

"I have. We have. We care deeply for each other, and *that,* Mason, is as far as we're going to take it."

"Levelheaded to the end," he said. There were days when he wished she weren't quite so sensible.

"To the end, Mason," she said.

In bed that night, Mason wondered what he would have done if Mary had told him that she and Priscilla were having a full-blown affair. What if she had said she wanted to leave him for her girlfriend?

He and Mary had chosen to make a life together, each for their own reasons, but ultimately, he guessed, because each of them had been a little lost, a little scared: Mary a young, soon-to-be divorced, lesbian mother; he a bookish, nerdy boy who couldn't imagine that there were guys out there like him, guys who might actually be attracted to him. *Chastity, isn't it about time you got banged in Boston?*

The first years of their marriage had been so happy: raising Ben together, building their respective careers, that quaint first apartment on Hereford Street. He was twenty-seven when he'd fallen into that first affair. He met Cameron, quite by accident, at a foreign-language bookstore in Harvard Square. They were both in the French section, Mason looking through a volume of Rimbaud; Cameron browsing through a copy of Cocteau's *Le Livre blanc.* Cameron began it.

"My guy," he said, holding up his copy of Cocteau, "thought he had to get out from under the spell of your guy." He nodded toward Mason's Rimbaud.

"And why is that?" Mason asked. He'd just bought his first pair of granny glasses, which he'd liked, but suddenly he worried that he looked awfully strait-laced and academic.

"Cocteau thought Rimbaud's influence was more of an encumbrance than a boost to his own expression. I'm writing my senior thesis on Cocteau."

Mason, who had always been a bit intimidated by Harvard students, decided it was time to push back a little.

"Every author," he said in French, "thinks the writers who came before him are encumbrances."

Cameron followed suit in French: "It's surprising, though, that Cocteau, a homosexual, should not have found at least some encouragement in Rimbaud's example."

They'd ended up going out for coffee on Brattle Street, where they talked (in a strait-laced and academic way) about French literature. Every time Cameron raised the issue of homosexuality, Mason steered them back into safer waters. After an hour, he said he had to get home. "But you'll have to come to dinner some night. I suspect my wife and I can feed you better than they do at Harvard."

Cameron's face fell.

"Did I say something wrong?" Mason asked.

"No, it's just that I've been talking to you for an hour, all along assuming you were gay." He seemed utterly nonchalant, and utterly amused, at his mistake. "I was actually going to invite you to be my guest for dinner tonight at Adams House."

"Well..." Mason said. He took off his granny glasses. "Well, I've never set foot in any of the august halls of Harvard. Do you suppose I could call my wife from your room?"

Their affair lasted four months. Mason was astounded by the intensity of Cameron's passion. Though he was only five years older than Cameron, he felt as if he belonged to another generation. What did this glorious boy find interesting in him, he kept fretting; when would Cameron realize how much less vibrant, less attractive, less *gay* Mason was?

Once a week, they had dinner at Adams House, in a dark wood-paneled dining hall graced with huge Georgian windows and full-length oil portraits of important-looking Harvard men who looked down upon them with utter self-assurance. Cameron's friends would sometimes join them, mostly other young men but a few women as well. They were all smart, rapid-fire conversationalists, who seemed, for the most part, to be into the arts — drama, music, dance. Mason had no idea whether they knew what was going on between him and Cameron, though he suspected they did. It did not seem to make any difference to them. The casualness with which Cameron's friends accepted this prep school French teacher into their circle was another thing that astonished him.

Cameron came from a very rich, very broken family. He was accustomed to taking his spring vacation in exotic places, Europe mainly. When he found out that the dates of his spring vacation coincided with Mason's at the Academy, he invited Mason to join him in southern France. All expenses paid. That's when Mason got cold feet. His wife, his kid, he pleaded. He couldn't just leave them. Didn't Cameron understand the difficulties? *You only live once*, Cameron argued. Mason told him he was being impetuously romantic. In a flash, he decided the thing had gone too far. Ben was ten years old that year, in some ways a more mature kid than Cameron.

* * *

In mid-October, the class finished the unit on Gide and commenced upon a study of French short stories. Since the students had already bought the anthology on Simone Dugied's list, Mason felt he had to assign it, and was happy to discover that at least three of the stories — the number he'd chosen for the unit — were totally acceptable to him. Aurore, Sabine and Nathan/Claude enjoyed them, but now it was Duncan's turn to be subdued. He was clearly unhappy that they had moved on from Gide and kept bringing up far-fetched theories about what he called "queer undercurrents" in the stories they were reading. The boy was hungry to keep pursuing the topic that had opened up when they'd read *The Notebooks of André Walter.*

One day, he stayed after class, trying to convince Mason of the homoeroticism — goodness, he had his gay lexicon down pat! — the homoeroticism in the stories by Maupassant and Camus that they were reading.

"You're reading too much into them," Mason told him. "You're projecting onto the text things that you *want* to see but that aren't there. These guys weren't gay, Dorian. There's nothing there to uncover."

"But what if, what if an author isn't aware of the homoerotic subtext that they've written into their story? I mean, come on, like *Billy Budd?* We just read that in English. Dude, it's a gay story whether Melville was gay or not."

"*Dude,*" he playfully fired back, "Maupassant is not Melville."

"So what about Proust? Are we going to read him this year?"

Mason laughed. "I'm afraid not, Dorian." He was tempted to add, *too difficult even for you.* Instead, he threw the boy a bone. "*Sois patient.* After this unit, we're going to do some poetry, including Rimbaud. I think Rimbaud's your man."

"Awesome!" Duncan yelped. "I've ready read a few of his poems. They're amazing."

Mason smiled. "He's one of my favorites. In fact, I've been working on translating some of his poems into English."

"Wow, really? Hey, if you'd ever like to show me... I mean, I'm sure you have other people you ask to read your translations — like your wife, I suppose — but, I mean, I'd be honored to read your versions."

"Actually, poetry is not my wife's thing. She's a psychologist. Mystery novels are more her kind of literature." This was more information about his marital life than he'd ever let out to any of his students. "So, in fact, I haven't shared my translations with her, or anyone."

A brief, awkward silence fell between them.

"So which Rimbaud poems will we be reading?" Duncan asked. "I mean, in class."

Mason tilted his head from side to side. "I haven't decided yet."

"What about *A Season in Hell?*" The boy was not to be stopped.

Mason's eyes widened and he jerked his head back theatrically. "Jesus! Is *that* the Rimbaud you've been reading?" He had never sworn in front of a student before. "Nothing like starting with the most difficult."

It was Duncan's turn to laugh. "Comes from reading all those Wikipedia articles, right?"

* * *

"The boy will not be stopped," Mason told Mary after he related the after-class conversation he'd had with Duncan. "He is so hungry for more. More Gide, more Rimbaud, more everything."

"Sounds like he has a healthy adolescent appetite for all that life has to offer," Mary said. "That's natural enough."

"Yes," Mason agreed. He went to the refrigerator, took out a half-opened bottle of wine, and held it out to Mary. She shook her head. He poured himself a glass and sat down at the kitchen table. "He seems curious about us, too. Keeps bringing you up. Today he wanted to know if you were the person I showed my translations to."

"That's sweet."

"I don't know. I've never told a student so much about my personal life before."

"It makes you uncomfortable?"

"*Comme si, comme ça.* Maybe I *want* to tell him about my life."

"What do you want to tell him?"

"What do I want to tell him?" he echoed. "There's a phrase in a poem by Rimbaud — *Soyez fous!* — Be foolish, be crazy. That's what I'd tell him. *Sois fou, Dorian!*"

Their eyes met. "Any regrets, Mason?" she asked.

"About?" She didn't answer. "Well, it's a little late for regrets, no?"

Mary laughed. "That's not much of an answer."

He studied his glass of wine. "Let's put it this way, darling: I think I've been as *fou* as" — now it was his turn to laugh — "as it was ever reasonable for me to be."

* * *

In November, Duncan approached Mason after class and told him about a reading that was going to take place the following Friday at the French Library in the Back Bay. A visiting professor from the West Coast would be debuting excerpts from a new Gide translation he was working on. Duncan could hardly contain himself, he was so excited at the prospect of attending the event. Mason said it might be an interesting outing for the whole class. And since the reading would take place at five o'clock, perhaps afterwards, they could all go out to a French restaurant for dinner.

It turned out that none of the other students could attend: Sabine had a tennis lesson on Friday evenings, Aurore said her mother — "my Chinese helicopter mom," she groused — wouldn't allow her to go into Boston at night. Nathan just said he couldn't make it, giving no particular reason. Mason wasn't sure about the propriety of a solo outing with just Duncan, but Krikorian told him he saw no harm in it — even the restaurant outing sounded like fun, he said — as long as Duncan had his parents' permission and he didn't drink any wine at dinner.

"Technically, I don't need my parents' permission to go," Duncan said when Mason outlined the provisions. "I'm already eighteen."

"Okay, but you're not free to drink wine," Mason told him.

"Hey, Rimbaud wrote *The Drunken Boat* when he was sixteen," Duncan said.

"You are *not* Rimbaud!"

"And I'm not sixteen." Mason couldn't read the expression on Duncan's face: it looked almost like a lascivious leer. He hoped the boy was teasing.

A few days before the reading, Mason decided to invite Mary to join him and Duncan. The program would be in English, he assured her. "And I think you'll enjoy meeting my star student," he added.

There were other reasons, too. Krikorian' permission notwithstanding, Mason knew he'd feel more comfortable if he didn't go to the lecture — and out to dinner — with only Duncan in tow.

"Sure," Mary said, "but when you originally told me you were taking the class out on Friday, I made plans with Priscilla for us to do something together. Would it be alright with you if I asked her to join us?"

"The more the merrier," Mason said.

* * *

The Professor's reading was prefaced by a short talk that he titled "*La Vie Hasardeuse:* Gide's Courageous Journey." He began his remarks with a quotation from *The Notebooks of André Walter* — "The young poet believes it is the Muse that inspires him when, in fact, it is puberty that leaves him aroused."

He looked up from his notes and smiled. The lecture room, which was being held in the French Library's parlor, was small enough that Mason could see the faces of several people in the audience. It appeared that half of them were gay men. Somehow, the word had gotten out that this lecture would be of particular interest to them.

Or maybe it was the Professor himself who was the big draw. He was young — Mason guessed in his early thirties — and strikingly handsome. Tall, svelte, athletically-sexy. Cascading over his forehead was a plume of tousled hair, which, from time to time, he would nonchalantly comb back with the fingers of his right hand. Instead of a suit or even sports jacket, he wore an open-collar shirt left untucked over a pair of close-fitting slacks. Despite the fact that it was now November, he was not wearing an undershirt. *Maybe,* Mason whispered to Mary, *that's how they all dressed at California universities these days.*

The Professor said that his research, and his translation work, were focused on the younger Gide — "that is," he clarified, "the Gide up through 1903, when he published *The Immoralist.*" It was this Gide, he said, who, "already unabashedly, *courageously*, set up the case for his defense of homosexuality, which he magnificently articulated in *Corydon.*"

Out of the corner of his eye, Mason saw that Duncan was fiercely scribbling away in his notebook.

After delivering his introduction, the Professor launched into his translation. "I'm going to read from Part II of *The Immoralist,*" he announced. "In this scene, the narrator, Michel — he's a kind of "blind-folded scholar," Gide says — is giving one of his Thursday evening at-homes with his wife. He knows his friends come because they are attracted to his wife's charm and conversation.

For himself, he is bored with the entire bourgeois social scene."

Mason saw Duncan close his notebook.

"In this first scene, Michel's friend Ménalque shows up at the Thursday evening at-home. Ménalque, whom Gide modeled after Oscar Wilde, lives a rather scandalous life. With a 'face like a pirate' and a drooping moustache, he disdains respectability and 'good society.' *J'aime la vie hasardeuse*, he tells Michel. 'I like the hazardous life, and I want it to demand of me, at every moment, all my courage, my wellbeing, my health.'"

The Professor began to read from his translation. Mason had last read *The Immoralist* during college. He'd forgotten just how outrageous a book it was. And how fresh, how, yes, courageous. He smiled to think what Mrs. Donohue might have said had he assigned his class excerpts from this novel.

He was sitting in the aisle seat of a row of gilded, faux-antique chairs. To his right were Duncan, then Mary, and last, farthest from the aisle, Priscilla. Mason wasn't sure how it happened that he had ended up seated next to Duncan. He guessed because Priscilla had taken her seat first, and Mary had slipped in next to her.

As the reading continued, Mason began to have the uncomfortable feeling that, whenever he glanced up from his paper, the Professor was making eye contact with him. He glanced over at Mary. All her attention was on the speaker.

The Professor wrapped up his first translation: "'What we feel is different in us from other people is precisely what is most exceptional.'" He looked up from his paper and, in a pretext of surveying the audience, once again made eye contact with... *My God*, Mason said to himself. *He's cruising Duncan!*

In the second scene that the Professor read, Michel visits Ménalque at his Paris hotel, and their conversation continues. "Here," the Professor told them, "Gide lays out even more explicitly the life philosophy he'd been developing. Michel asks his friend why he doesn't write his memoirs." He looked down at his manuscript and began to read: "Regrets, remorse, repentances: these are earlier joys, backward-looking prospects..."

As the Professor continued reading, Mason let his mind wander... back to the eighth grade and Gordie's darkroom, back to his days at the University of New Hampshire and his fraternity brothers, back to meeting Mary. As much as he loved Gide, he couldn't imagine ever behaving the way Gide had: consorting with Arab boys, cruising the boulevards and swimming pools, the restless traveling, the shabby pulling away from his marriage. No, he had chosen a very different path from that one. He'd made it work. Perhaps he'd even nailed it.

The reading ended, the audience applauded, in turn they were thanked and invited to ask questions. Duncan's hand shot up.

"What do you think Gide would say about the LGBTQIA+ movement today?"

Several people in the audience turned to see who had asked such a goofy, bold, adolescent question. Mason glanced over at Mary, who raised her eyes surreptitiously.

"It's an excellent question," the Professor said. He went on to give his opinion. Mason heard none of it. All he heard was the flirtatious ardor in the Professor's voice.

"Thank you," Duncan said, when the Professor had finished.

"Mon plaisir," said the Professor.

There were a few more questions and then the audience was invited for champagne and hors d'oeuvres in the salon.

Mason glanced at his watch. It was six-fifteen. Their dinner reservation at the French restaurant was for seven. He looked at Mary and Priscilla.

"Shall we stay a few minutes?"

"Why not? But keep an eye on the boy," Mary said, nodding over to the refreshment table, where Duncan had already wandered. "We don't want him getting soused on free champagne."

They made their way to the table. Duncan had already been approached by a few of members of the audience — all men of a certain age, Mason noticed — who seemed to want to talk to him. When one of them offered Duncan a glass of champagne, Mason was relieved to see that Duncan shook his head no.

The three adults — Mary, Priscilla and Mason — stood around drinking champagne and talking. Priscilla said she had found the lecture fascinating. It had renewed her interest in reading *The Pastoral Symphony.* Mason again told her not to waste her time, that she'd be better off reading *The Immoralist.*

Priscilla laughed. "I feel as if I should start with the 'less dangerous' one first." She made air quotes around "less dangerous."

"Why the hell do that!" Mason snapped. It startled him, the combative tone that had suddenly arisen in his voice. "Weren't you listening? *La vie hasardeuse:* living hazardously, living with all your courage." He realized he'd probably had too much champagne.

"There are many kinds of courage," Priscilla said.

"Yes, *many* kinds," he fired back, still unable to curb the disagreeable note in his voice. "And Gide's kind strikes me as exceptional."

"That's the word, isn't it?" Priscilla said. "'Exceptional.' Not everyone is capable of that degree of bravery" — she paused — "that degree of recklessness, I'd say." A frostiness had crept into her voice. "It's okay, you know, for people to live their lives, well, more *moderately* than your darling Gide did, and yet still live with integrity."

"Yes, I'm quite aware of that, Priscilla." Now it was his turn to pause. And then to let out a snicker: "I guess I didn't realize I was coming here for *two* lectures." Mason felt himself getting red in the face. Here was his wife's former lover spouting to him his very own life's doctrine, and it was pissing him off. "Yes, my dear, not all of us can be exceptional, can we?"

Mary gently touched his arm.

"Mason, it's getting late for our reservation." She made brief eye contact with Priscilla. "I think we should probably get going."

Mason took in a deep breath. At the moment, going out to dinner, especially with Priscilla in tow, was the last thing he wanted. As for what he *did* want, he couldn't say. This whole outing was suddenly feeling like a bad idea. Or maybe he should have stuck to the original plan: just inviting Duncan and no one else. He looked toward the hors d'oeuvre table. Duncan had disappeared. Sourly, he told Mary and Priscilla he'd go find the boy.

As he made his way through the crowd, he caught snippets of conversations. "The Dorothy Bussy translation is still my favorite," he overheard one man say. Another exclaimed, "What a cutie."

Who? Mason wanted to ask. He felt his animosity rising again, now directed to these pretentious gay men and their tittering prurience. But where the hell was Duncan? He was about to return to Mary and Priscilla when he caught sight of the boy. He had gone back to the lecture room and was talking to the Professor, who was packing up his briefcase. As he approached them, Duncan saw him and called out.

"Monsieur Chastain!"

Introductions were made, handshakes exchanged, compliments from Mason received by the Professor. Mason hoped the men back in the salon were noticing the exclusive little trio he had formed with these two beautiful young men. *That's* what he wanted right now: someone to be jealous of him.

"Um, sir, would it be okay with you if I skipped the restaurant?" Duncan asked. "The Professor has asked me to join him and his husband for dinner on Beacon Hill."

Before Mason had a moment to recover from the surprise, Mary and Priscilla wandered over. More introductions. The Professor looked at Mary and Priscilla and smiled knowingly. *There's nothing to know,* Mason thought.

"It seems that Duncan won't be joining us for dinner," he told Mary.

"Oh!" She searched Mason's face, trying to gauge his stand.

"I was just about to tell him that it was okay with me." Mason turned to Duncan. "As long as you have a way to get home."

"Of course," Duncan said. "I'll take the T."

"And…" Mason added. This was awkward but he had to say it. "You will remember that the drinking age in Massachusetts in twenty-one."

The Professor laughed and patted Duncan on the shoulder. "We'll see to it that he remembers."

"We'll miss your company, Duncan," Mary said. She turned to Priscilla. "But I guess these three old folks can still have a good time, no?"

"Absolutely!" Priscilla said in her husky, mannish voice.

"Well, then," Mason said, "may everyone, each in his own way, have a lovely evening."

"Bon soir."

"Bon soir."

It was a mild November evening. As they left the Library, Mason made sure to position himself between Mary and Priscilla. He took Mary's hand. In return, she squeezed his, her way — she had been doing it all their married life — of saying, *Yes, I'm right here.*

Mason wondered if he should have insisted on Duncan's staying with them. But, yes, the boy was eighteen, technically, *legally,* an adult and able to make his own decisions. He was choosing to be among those "singing fish on the blue tide." *And why not,* Mason thought. *Why not?*

The magnolia trees along Commonwealth Avenue were dropping their yellow leaves. The sidewalk was strewn with them. They made a crinkling sound under his feet. *Years from now,* Mason thought, *Duncan would come to cherish this evening. To see it as something exceptional. And to feel,* Mason hoped, *a touch of gratitude for his old French teacher, who had, in his own modest way, allowed the boy a taste of the hazardous life.*

Silently, he reached over and took Priscilla's hand. Startled, she looked over at him, smiled, and said nothing. They entered the restaurant, the three of them, hand in hand in hand.

The Trunk of Boothbay Harbor

Charles Townsend

Every June, for eight years since the end of the war, the Pilsner family traveled to Maine. For the last six of those years, their daughter Helen went with them. For the seventh year, the final year, their baby son, Albert, traveled with them as well. It would be the last time the Pilsner family set foot in Boothbay Harbor.

"Sleep" by Fred Waring & the Pennsylvanians played softly from the scratchy radio in the front seat. Helen and the others bumped when Pop's 1925 Ford ran over the occasional rock. Rapidly alternating green-tinted shadows and late-morning light illuminated the interior from the frames of the open windows. A dark strip of clouds in the distance inched closer. It would snuff out their window of sunshine before the day was out.

Baby Albert, called Alb, gazed up at Helen in her yellow dress and blonde hair with big, curious eyes from his cradle to the right of her. In his hand was a new toy her mother had gotten him, likely no more than a week old. Like all the other toys. She glared at him and held her old doll close. To her left, big brother Andy pulled on his smelly cigarette and flashed smiles and waves outside the window to the rare passing vehicle or walker. He wore his brown uniform, like he always did. The cuffs fine, the fabric spotless, the tie and lapels tight and neat. No light or flickering shadows came in from the back seat, as it was filled to the ceiling with luggage.

In the driver's seat, Pa kept his eyes hard on the road. The corners of his mouth and eyes curled upwards in a cheery, relaxed smile. His suit jacket was off, and his suspenders clamped down his thin, sweaty dress shirt. Tufts of graying hair puffed out from his hatless head. To his right, Mother knit away at a scarf. Her blonde hair was tucked away cleanly under her black cloche hat. Jewelry hung from her neck.

"Heyo Pa, what's the time?" Andy asked after a pull from his cigarette.

"Hm," he said, checking his watch. "We'll be there soon."

"Soon, soon... but what's the time?"

"It'll be another half an hour or less."

"Pop, just the time, what's the—"

Mother spoke up. "Get over the time, Andrew! Heavens, must you always ask for the time every several minutes?"

"Ma, I just wanna know the time!"

"Perhaps if you bought your own watch instead of losing your money in cards with your friends—"

"God! It's always about my friends with you, isn't it? Always these comments about how I spend my money and time—"

"Enough!" Mr. Pilsner roared. "It's five after eleven."

They were all quiet after that.

The trees and grass glittered from the early morning rainfall. Cows from neighboring fields watched them go by with glassy, lazy eyes. Boothbay Harbor was too familiar to be exciting to either Andy or Helen. She couldn't talk to him, though. He was too distracted. Too old for her and for talking. He needed excitement, things to see and do on his own. He was reluctant enough as it was to join them on the trip.

"But you've got no wife or family," Ma had told him when he protested. "And no place of your own."

That bothered him.

When they arrived at Boothbay Harbor, Andy looked around even more distractedly than before. His gaze stayed on a passing group of girls more than once. He'd wave at them wearing his big smile and they'd maybe wave back or giggle. Salty ocean air wafted in. Helen fixed her eyes on her doll and tried to ignore his shifting motions next to her. At the Boothbay Harbor Grand Hotel, they parked on the roadside. The Grand Hotel would be considered grand compared to the town, but compared to other hotels in bigger tourist locations it'd hardly be considered second-rate. The hotel was nothing more to Helen and Andy as "the place they stayed for a week" each June. Familiarity kills the attraction of mystery and novelty.

The brick building loomed four stories overhead, arcing out by its top with flagging, buttress-like stone. The first floor was not brick but large blocks of limestone. As soon as they parked, a door-boy in a purple suit walked up to them with a wheeled rack. The Pilsners opened the back doors of the automobile and allowed the bellhop and another one to unload their luggage, which was also strapped to the roof. Mrs. Pilsner had brought too much, as per usual.

Dark, shuttered windows lined the hotel front. Below each row of windows was a long, stone ledge carved with Atlantic patterns of ropes and anchors. They walked through the doors and entered a marble and wood interior; a mix of fancy and local. A glittering chandelier over a circle rug, the centerpiece, sent sparkling rays from the electric lights lining the corridor. Helen and Andy immediately took seats by the wall, Helen tasked with carrying Alb in his cradle. She lugged the cradle over and dumped it on the floor, gentle enough to not make him cry but aggressively enough to signal to Andy that she wasn't interested in doing the labor. He wasn't paying attention; his head was turned in the direction of a pretty woman at the end of the hall reading from a folio. Helen returned her glare back to baby Albert. He met her eyes with his own, and he let out a high-pitched cackle and reached up at her with little fists. She crossed her arms.

The family was led upstairs to the second floor. They knew the way up, being regulars at the hotel for the past decade. Mr. Pilsner paid off the door boys who took up their baggage. Inside, their rooms were plain and lacked the grandeur of the foyer, but were homey. Yellow and white wallpaper reflected the light let in from the windows once Pop opened them. The boards creaked under their footsteps. Helen begrudgingly accepted the couch in the side room, as always. Andy got his own room and key, which left Helen more sour than before. His room was connected to hers by use of a door locked on both sides. Neither of them intended to use that door. Her room had a closet where the door to the hallway would've been, making her only exit Andrew's room and her parents' room. And the window, if she was counting that at all.

Even worse, Albert would be staying in her room, too. He never cried, which was unusual enough to get mother concerned at times, but that wasn't the thing that bothered her.

"Pretty fine, eh, gal?" Pa said, rubbing her head. She took a step away from him, her doll tucked against her chest from her crossed arms. He sighed. "Yeah, yeah that'll... mm."

She closed the door to her side room and plopped herself onto the couch. It was springy and not cushy. She growled and slid off of it, pulling out the three drawers of the bureau instead. Empty, empty, empty. Crossing the room and the large carpet that dominated it, she went to the closet. When she opened it she took a step back, a mix of surprise and curiosity on her face. Inside the closet, barely able to fit, was a trunk. A foot shorter than she was, sitting on its long side, the trunk was a dark gray, with tarnished and aged metal corners and clasps. Old scratches and nicks marked its leather sides, which were so old and battered she wasn't even sure if it was still leather. Weathered stickers from past hotels and trips with indecipherable words dotted the exterior. Little light illuminated the closet, leaving the trunk mostly cloaked in darkness, save some of its front side.

Sounds from Ma and Pa died out. A special sort of gravity of silence radiated from the trunk. A bending of time, sight, and sound. For a moment, just a moment, Helen forgot about the trip. Forgot about her parents, Andy, and Albert. Forgot about the whole entire world.

It was just she, the girl, and it, the trunk.

A rough hand landed on her shoulder and she jumped, holding her doll close. The gravity and silence snapped away from existence. He looked down at her with curious eyes, one of his eyebrows raised suspiciously.

"What ya got here, sis? I don't remember packing that for the way up."

"Oh, it's... I—"

"Say, this isn't ours! Maybe we should go tell the hotel staff that someone left their luggage."

"No!" she said. He tilted his head and narrowed his eyes at her sudden burst. "No," she said again, "It's...."

"Ya know, I think you got a point there now that I think of it. How'd that even get in there? It looks too big and wide for the doorway...."

He leaned closer and peeked his head into the closet to look at either end of the trunk. It was indeed too big to have been fit through the doorway. He frowned, but didn't question it any longer.

"Well, not our problem, at least. Poor sucker who got it stuck in here in the first place has some thinking to do about where he places his luggage."

He popped open the clasps and Helen gasped quietly, as if he just committed a sacrilegious act, but he didn't notice. A jolt of fear shook her as he opened the trunk, but was soon settled. She took a step forward to see the trunk was empty. Blue-patterned wallpaper covered all sides. A musty air bellowed out and Andy waved a hand through the air to disperse it. He suddenly closed the trunk and Helen winced. Each touching of the trunk disturbed her, like touching it was touching a house of cards or a delicate object.

When he wandered off to the other room where Mr. and Mrs. Pilsner were discussing plans for the afternoon, much-needed relief filled Helen. She took in a few deep breaths, and then sat down, cross-legged to gaze at the trunk. Sounds of footsteps from the other room, coming closer, creaked the floorboards. Her eyes went wide. No one else must know about the trunk. No one else except her. She realized letting Andy see it at all was a foolish mistake. She shot up and slammed the closet door shut just when her father opened her own door and walked in. He gave her an odd look.

"Slamming doors, sweetie? Not very polite to the other guests of the hotel."

She broke from her stupor. "Yes, yes. I know. I'm sorry. The door, it was — it was stuck, and when I closed it, it shut really heavy."

He stared at her long enough to make her think that he didn't believe her, but then he chuckled. "Better not use that closet, then."

"Yes, better not."

"Um..." he tapped his fingers on the doorknob. "What was it? Ah, right! We're going to get some lunch in us. Don't take your shoes off or settle in too quickly."

"Okay, Pop."

He smiled and closed the door softly behind her.

Her chest and face fell. That was close. So very close.

Baby Albert let out some amused baby sounds from his cradle. She flicked her eyes to him and watched him for a few moments, her relief having turned into a fearful irritation. He was just a baby, though. It would be okay; Andy was the one she had to worry about. Oh yes, yes....

She straightened the ribbon in her hair and stepped away from the closet to get ready.

* * *

The clouds had taken Boothbay Harbor, working as a cloak which dimmed the sun fighting to maintain the daylight. Rains would come later. The Pilsners ate their lunch and were going to go on a walk around the harbor when Mr. Pilsner deemed it a good idea to head back to the hotel. The stillness before a storm, misty and ominous, had filled the air. And he was right; as afternoon turned into later afternoon, and eventually evening, the clouds gushed down sheets of rain which pounded the roof of the Boothbay Harbor Grand Hotel. They ate the hotel dinner, which wasn't half bad, although Andy drank too much when he left the family to go to the bar. Mrs. Pilsner was about to stop him before he did so, but Mr. Pilsner allowed him.

"A boy's gotta learn his limits and enjoy his youth," he said.

"That boy of ours is twenty-five years of age!"

"Leave him be."

"Hmph," she said, claiming her wine glass and turning away to sip it. Mr. Pilsner laughed and continued slaying his fish and chips. Baby Albert let out a squeaky laugh with him, which made the father smile.

"Ma? Pa?" Helen asked in a sweet, darling voice. "May I go back to the room? I'm not feeling so good."

"Was it something in your chicken? I swear to God, these people never even fixed their chicken since three years ago when I—" Mr. Pilsner stopped himself after catching Helen's pleading eyes. "Ah, sure, fine. Scurry off. Your mother and I will enjoy dessert, though! Make sure to open the door for us when we come back in an hour or two, heh!"

He handed her his key.

"Thank you, father."

She excused herself and made back to the stairs. The carpet quieted her footfalls as she got to the room. Turning the key in the lock, she looked left. She looked right. Nobody; not a soul. Then she twisted the knob and walked in. She didn't bother with the lights. Her feet took her quickly back to the closet, which she opened slowly and carefully. Yes, there it still was. Its hard, gray exterior. Its withered shell of scars and stickers. Its tarnished, aged clasps and corners. Her hand reached out, and when her fingertips grazed the surface, a cold sensation shot through her. Her hand flattened so that from her fingertips to her palm, her whole hand pressed against its surface. A thin layer of dust rolled as she ran her hand against the top. She brought her second hand to it and felt the metal seam. Her hands found the clasps, and with a jolt of fear and curiosity, she undid them, opening it up and backing away. Nothing inside. Like last time.

Her doll sat against the wall, motionless and silent. She grabbed it and, leaning in, placed it in the trunk. A long shadow trailed away from it and onto the wall, next to hers. Its button eyes stared lifelessly up at her. Darkness slithered further into the interior as she steadily closed the trunk. Metal clinked metal as she did the clasps. Then she backed away, as if expecting the trunk to do something. But it did not do anything. It sat there, quiet in the twilight stretching in from the one window across the room.

Her hands hastily undid the clasps, as if she had waited too long in her experiment. But when she opened the trunk, its blue-patterned, wallpaper sides was all she saw.

Empty.

* * *

Helen couldn't go to sleep that night. In the twilight darkness, the curtains open to let in shades of moonlight, her eyes stuck out as two bright whites. The closet door was open a few inches, just enough for her to see the trunk. A sliver of moonlight slipped through this opening, leaving a slice of illumination over the dusty, gray sides.

She had laid that way for two hours.

Where had her doll gone to? She did not know. She had tried closing and opening it again and again after that, but the doll never came back. It left her with a gripping fascination before her father made her go to bed — she was lucky she closed the closet door in time before he walked in.

But before he interrupted her, she had put in hairs, buttons, a spare shoelace, a pin, and a pair of socks. All disappeared. All were snapped from the memory of existence, like a reverse-photograph. The trunk closed, and then opened, and whatever was placed inside was gone. Gone to where? God only knows. Gone to that strange space between imagination and reality, where something may have existed, but its only proof of existence was in the mind of a child.

And it filled her with a terrible hunger.

Baby Albert broke her contemplative silence with an "ack-cack" sound. She sat up on the couch and gazed down to the cradle next to her, as if she were seeing it for the very first time. A basket, really, with cloth padding and an awning over one side. Her eyes sparkled in the moonlight. Her legs slipped out from her bed, and barefoot she took a few steps to stand over the cradle. Alb turned his head to her and smiled playfully. She stood there a moment, and licked her lips, thinking deep and long. The next movements she took were so measured, so clean in their simple grace, she might have been in a trance. She picked up the cradle, and Alb giggled quietly. Her feet led her slowly to the closet. With one hand, she opened the closet door. Her silhouette arced over the trunk; a stripe of shadow in the surrounding moonlight. She placed baby Albert down and undid the clasps. A quiet whining sounded as the trunk opened to reveal its dark, musty, blue-and-white interior. She lifted the cradle, with baby Albert still in it, and lowered it into the trunk like a deep-sea diver into the depths. He clenched his little baby fists. He was suddenly shrouded in shadow, her shadow, when she leaned back up and peered down at him. He looked around before resting his curious eyes on her, a silly, drooling grin on his face.

He gave a "cack" one last time before she closed the trunk and did the clasps. When she opened it, the trunk was as it was before; blue, white, and silent.

She went back to bed.

* * *

No more than a half an hour later, when she was still awake and staring at the ceiling, did the muted sound of a door smashing open sound from a room next to her meet her ears. A "goodnight sweet thing" and then a much quieter closing of a door. A giggle. A thump against a bed.

She walked over to the door she shared with Andy and knocked three times. Three times loud enough so only he could hear. A grumble and then padded footsteps. The lock clinked as a key was shoved into it, and she put her own key in and turned it. The door swung open and nearly knocked her over. She shielded her eyes as bright, yellow light poured in.

Her eyes acclimated, and although he wasn't facing the light, she could still make out his features. His tie was undone, and so was his jacket; the buttons loose and askew as if it was opened hastily. His hair was ruffled and messy, and had a cowlick going on one side. His eyes were lazy and unfocused, and he swayed on his feet.

"Yeah an', an' whadd'you want, Helly?"

"Helen, Andy."

"Mm."

"Um, there's something weird about that trunk in the closet."

"Where's 'im... where's Alb?"

"Sleeping with Ma, but come to the trunk. There's something weird about it."

He stumbled over with a groan, slapping his key down against her nightstand. The staccato clap of it against the wood made her jump. He didn't notice or didn't care. She led him across the room to the trunk, and he stood over it.

"Inside," she said.

He clumsily undid the clasps and peered inside.

"Don't you see that weird thing in the seam of the back side and the bottom?"

"Hrmmg, no."

"Look closer, it's there!"

"What is it?"

"I think it's a dollar bill! Maybe a ten-dollar bill, hidden beneath the wallpaper but the end just peeking out!"

"Oh? Hmm...." he mumbled, leaning over. Then he slumped a leg over, and the other over, and crouched down in the space to inspect the seam. "Don't really see... hey—"

He jerked up as she slammed the trunk cover down, and it hit his head with a clunk. The cover closed, but was inched open as fingers gripped the top of the front side. She slammed the trunk closed again and again onto his fingers, and the hand coiled back in with a curse. Her hands went immediately to the clasps, and then all was quiet. She waited a minute. Two minutes. Her parents did not wake up. Undoing the clasps, she looked inside.

Nothing.

She swallowed and a thrill ran through her. Quietly, she opened the window to her room. Cool midnight air breezed past her, flapping the curtains. Grabbing the key he had snapped against the nightstand, she went into his room, locking the door to her room behind her. She also locked the front door that led into the hallway. She grabbed a chair from the desk and shoved it under the doorknob for good measure. Then, turning off the lights, she slipped both keys into her pocket and opened the curtains to the window. The soft, silver glow sent pale rays across the room.

On the bureau was a single candlestick, long, ornate, but made of thick pewter. It glittered in the dim light. Helen approached it. She had to leap up to grab it, but soon it was in her clutches. Heavy, and widening at the bottom. She hesitated before deciding to bring it with her.

With effort she slid up the window. Nobody was in the harbor town street, and no light came from any windows. She stepped out onto the ledge, closing the window behind her. The stone was cool under her bare feet. Her blonde hair rustled as a stronger wind came, and she pressed herself against the side of the building. Her heart pounded rapidly in her chest. But the thrill pushed her on. Kept her moving. Got her across that ten feet to her window, where she climbed back in and she closed it behind her.

The plan was solidified in her head before she knew it. She took in a deep breath, but it had to be done. The candlestick thumped against the carpet when it slid from her small hand. She opened the trunk and placed her key at the bottom and didn't close it. Her brother's own key rested in her pocket. Going to the bureau, she opened the lowest drawer and put her forearm against the corner of where the top edge of the left side of the drawer slid into the compartment. Then she pushed it slowly closed. Her skin was caught between the drawer and the bureau corner, in a too-small space, squeezing and dragging it. She stomached a scream and bit her fist, pushed the drawer in more with her knees. Tears of pain welled up in her eyes before streaming down her face. The coolness of the tears made her stop, and she felt her skin there — red, raw, and sensitive. That was good enough.

"Mama! Papa! Mama!" she burst through the door connecting their rooms and spilled herself over the bed, beating it with her fists as she feigned violent crying.

The light flickered on.

"Oh darling, what's wrong?" her mother asked, taking her into her arms.

"Mama! Andy took Albert, he-he took him into his room! He's drunk, he's... oh Mama!"

"That boy!" her father roared, whipping off the sheets and swiping off his nightcap in a red, hairy fist. "I'll get him, I swear!"

"He locked the door to my room, he has girls in there, too!"

Mr. Pilsner bustled out of the room into the hallway, leaving the door ajar. Her mother held her close and shushed her in a low, childish voice.

"Mama," she said. "Mama, he... come here."

She took her mother's hand and led the woman into her room. The banging of Mr. Pilsner's fist on the front door to Andy's room sounded. A few hotel guests above them uttered swears.

"See the trunk, Mama?"

She led her to the trunk. Her mother tilted her head at it and looked in as she opened it.

"What about this trunk, darling?"

Helen's fingers grasped the cool metal end of the candlestick. Her footsteps were soundless on the carpet. "Do you see what's inside? My key's in there!"

Mr. Pilsner slammed his fist against the front door some more. "Open up, you little brat! You no-good...."

Mrs. Pilsner coughed from the dust. "Oh, yes, I see! Very good you have your own key, just gotta reach...."

Helen wielded the candlestick high in the air above her mother and then clapped it hard against the back of her head with a thunk. The woman collapsed forward into the trunk, unconscious. Helen closed it and clasped it. When she undid the clasps and opened it once more, her mother was not inside. Her mother was not anywhere at all. She threw her brother's key in there and left it open. Helen put the candlestick down in front of the bureau on her way out.

She ran back to her parents' room and then into the hallway. Her father still clutched his nightcap in one hand and pounded the door with the other. His white gown sloped down his chest to hang at the ankles. If his feet weren't there, he might've been a ghost.

"Papa! Papa!" she said, stopping him before other guests of the hotel could leave their rooms to complain about the ruckus. "Papa! Mama went into the room through my door!"

"What?"

"Come!"

She ran back to her room, with her father in close pursuit.

"You open this door right now, mister, or I'm coming in there!" he said, going to the side door between the rooms.

"Why is no one speaking in there?"

"He's drunk, Papa, he cupped Mama's mouth and—"

"That little — that rat, that amphibian!"

"Papa, the trunk! He put my key in the trunk! I can't reach it, though!"

"A key, eh?" he asked, walking over to the trunk.

He looked inside, then leaned down to claim the key on the trunk bottom.

She thumped him on the back of the head. A gasp of half pain and half shock escaped him. He lurched back and stumbled into the bureau, falling to the floor as he clutched his head. A crazed, malicious grin gazed down at him. Helen struck at his head again, and again, and again until she heard a crack. He lay motionless. Speckles of blood on the carpet. Hastily, she dropped the candlestick and started lugging him across the floor. It took her a minute or two to bring him all the way to the trunk, lugging him inch by inch. She pulled over a chair to slump his legs onto. And then another chair from the other room — which she locked from the outside with Papa's key. Using these chairs, she was able to prop him up, although it took a great deal of effort. She slugged one leg into the trunk, and then the other leg, and then an arm. Pushing with all her might, her knees buckling and her teeth gritting, he eventually toppled in.

Helen slammed the trunk closed and did the clasps. Then she was alone again.

She breathed in heavy breaths, stepping back from the trunk. Sleepy and angry hotel guests thundered down the hallway, mumbling to themselves.

She undid the clasps and opened the trunk.

Inside, enveloped in her shadow sharp against the light, was a doll with buttons for eyes, sitting still. She picked it up and walked away from the trunk. As she entered the hallway, a mustached man in a nightgown and cap glared down at her.

"Where on God's green Earth is that man making all that noise?"

She said nothing to him. He lingered by her for a moment but dismissed her with a wave and a scoff. He and a few others trailed into the room she left as Helen took the stairs down, passed through the foyer undisturbed, and entered the night with her doll held close. The road was cool under her feet. A calm breeze played with the ends of her hair and the hems of her nightclothes. Then she was gone.

On the Beach / Rain

Michael Paul Hogan

Harry's 1958 Thunderbird turned off the road and onto the beach. All four doors swung open and each of us got out. It was six in the morning and the beach was deserted. The sea was purple and the sky was orange and the horizon a thin line of green. Harry took a handgun out of the glove compartment and started shooting at an empty Budweiser bottle that Billy Ray had thrown out into the sea. Billy Ray took another bottle out of the crate in the trunk and went and stood over on Harry's left, watching the spurts of water the bullets kicked up, tilting the beer in a long, smooth swallow while Harry reloaded out of a box on the driver's seat. Eight-Ball Eddie had wandered off up the shoreline some ways and was holding a bottle of Four Roses and skimming coins across the surface of the sea. I felt a little cold and kind of sat, kind of leaned back against the hood of the Thunderbird, gripping my own bottle of Bud between my knees while I lit a cigarette. I'd had the idea of a story taking better and better shape in my mind during the whole time we were in The Blue Parrot. It had survived the noise of the jukebox and a whole load of tequila shots and eight or nine games of pool and it would be sad to lose it now, now that we were out at the beach. I inhaled and exhaled and imagined I was in my college room and sitting in front of my Remington portable and typing it down. *It had been raining for nine days. The color had long ago bleached out of the world and the cupolas and the domes and the rooftops were pewter-gray.* Imagining typing a story was a good way not to lose it. I visualized the keys hammering a sheet of paper and mentally slammed the carriage shift each time Harry shot a bullet into the sea.

* * *

It had been raining for nine days. The color had long ago bleached out of the world and the cupolas and the domes and the rooftops were pewter-gray. Even the sky was saturated, and it rippled in the breeze like a photograph in a developing tray. She said, "Do you remember Thailand? It rained so hard the street became a river. A boy caught a fish with a fishing rod from the balcony opposite our apartment."

"I remember."

"And that time in Key Blanco? People rowed boats down Perry Street. We waded knee-deep to buy groceries at the store."

"I remember that too."

She laughed. She said, "You're a writer. You're a cheat! You remember everything!"

The rain was like a slender curtain between their veranda and the rest of a saturated world. A fine mist of dampness permeated the air. They could feel it on the rims of the glasses from which they drank and breathed it as a fisherman might breathe in a fog. He said, "It's strange. It's as though each day of rain is washing away another layer of recent history, exposing forgotten layers of the past..."

* * *

He remembered walking along a beach somewhere in the tropics, with the sea on his right and palm trees on his left. There was no sound at all, no birds either visible or hidden in the foliage, and the sea was as still as a bowl of mercury. Ahead of him, drawn up on the sand so far that it was nearly in the shade of the palm trees, there was a boat, an obviously abandoned boat, in length about thirty feet, barely listing, its stern extending almost half-way to the edge of the sea.

He reached up and ran his fingertips along the gunwale. It had the texture of stippled plaster and contained traces of the original red and blue paint on the crumbling ridges. The name of the boat, once stenciled in black letters, was now too faded and weather-worn to make out, but he intuited, he *knew*, that it was the name of a girl the owner of the boat had loved but had lost while he was out at sea. And then suddenly, as though the curtain had been raised on a vast stage — *no*, as though the curtain had dissolved as he had walked through it — he saw a young woman standing in the shallows, holding up the hem of her dress with one hand and shielding her eyes with the other. The distance between them was no more than twenty feet and yet she seemed very far away. It would have been no more possible to call out to her than to call out to a ship on the horizon, but he remembered an overwhelming urge to speak to her, to be the focus of her attention even if only for a moment or two. Then the memory rippled and faded and he was again alone on a tropical beach next to an abandoned boat that seemed to hold within its timbers all the salt of a thousand days at sea.

* * *

He smiled at the memory. He said, "Would you like another drink?"

"In a minute, when I've finished this one. What were you remembering? You were very far away."

"A boat abandoned on a beach. A girl. But it wasn't like a memory. More like a waking dream."

"Dreams are only shattered memories, put back together by the mad and blind," she replied.

The veranda upon which they stood had four steps leading down to a semi-circular patio surrounded by lawn. The lawn was entirely underwater, the grass-blades an expanse of flowering coral, and the rain had covered the patio to the elevation of the first of the steps. She said, "It's like a swimming pool. When I was a child, I always wanted a swimming pool. I wanted to dive into it wearing a skin-tight one-piece ivory-colored bathing suit. Like on the cover of *Vogue*."

She raised the hem of her dress with her left hand and descended the steps. She looked over her shoulder. She said, "Do you remember?"

"Remember what?"

"When I was reading Holberg's *Subterranean Voyage of Nicholas Klimn* and eating the box of chocolates you'd given me because I'd caught you smiling at some girl on the Auto-Shuttle –"

"I remember the chocolates. I don't remember the girl."

"– and I flattened out the foil that had been wrapped around the crème noisette and used it as a bookmark. And the more I used it and the more flattened it got the more beautiful it became. A sort of meeting point between poetry and spatial physics. Or better still the after-image caused by a combination of Rayographs and driving very fast down Fifth Avenue on a late December afternoon in the pouring sleet and rain. Oh, and incidentally, the girl was memorable, the chocolates were not."

"But you remembered the chocolates."

"But you failed to remember the girl."

He went over to the drinks trolley that was parked just beside the French doors that led back into their villa and poured himself another martini. She said, "What was I wearing when we first met?"

"We met at a party on Moon-Base Nine."

"That isn't the answer to the question I asked."

"It's the answer to the question that should've come first," he retorted.

"What was I wearing?" she repeated.

"You were wearing toreador pants and a white cotton shirt. What was I wearing?"

She thought for a moment and then shook her head. "I can't remember. I remember the gin ran out and the vol-au-vents were cold. I remember it was snowing outside. I remember I went out onto the balcony because someone had given me a brandy and I needed some fresh air. It was the most wonderful, the freshest air I had ever known. I lit a cigarette and almost immediately a snowflake, an absolutely *enormous* snowflake, landed *sssssssss* on the head of the match. I'd never seen such a perfect snowflake before — and haven't since. And while I was smoking the cigarette, I looked over the balcony railing and down at the street. I think we were four, maybe five floors up. And although the party wasn't a very wonderful party, in fact it was really rather second-rate, they'd done a fantastic job of setting up an exterior facsimile of Prague and I remember looking down at the tramlines glittering or gleaming or whatever through the cobblestones, and a streetlight illuminating a poster for the Black-Light Theatre, and everything, all of this, seen through a sort of screen of snow, and seen falling *down*, away from one, so that the flakes of snow were spinning, *spinning* between oneself and the street. And I remember the exact texture of the cigarette filter between my lips as I saw a man down on the street, he must've stepped off the departing tram, wearing an overcoat with the collar turned up and a hat with a gorgeously swooping brim and surrounded by—"

"By?"

"—by snowflakes. And then he glanced up at where I was standing, smiled a slender smile, and walked in the direction of the Old Town Square. I remember wanting to call out to him or something, I didn't know what, I took the cigarette out of my mouth and was waving it like it was a children's firework toy, and then another star came and sat on the end of my cigarette and went *sssssssss* just like before..."

"A star? Don't you mean snowflake?" he asked.

"...I mean something beautiful and incredible that fell from the sky. Who knows? There is less difference between a snowflake and a star than there is between a man who steps off a tram and glances up at a balcony and a man who stays on the tram and is merely a silhouette in a square of yellow light..."

He stepped down just behind her, on the lowest dry step, and handed her a lighted cigarette. She let the hem of her dress fall to receive it and glanced down at the flimsy cotton half-floating half-sinking in the clear martini-colored water. She smiled. She said, "In the depths of the deepest sea, in depths deeper even than those discerned of by Professor Apollinax or Nicholas Krimn, there exist creatures that unspool their intestines as a faulty film projector might unspool the works of Jean-Luc Godard, leaving behind them a gorgeous phosphorescence, illuminating with celluloid the submarine."

"*Vivre sa vie* with Anna Karina."

"*The Oval Portrait* by Edgar A. Poe."

"Where did we meet — the second time?" he asked.

"In a taxi we shared by sheer coincidence."

"From where to where?"

"From somewhere in the Village to East Fifty-third Street."

"What was I wearing? Can you remember?" he asked.

"A black polo-neck sweater and a pair of green-tinted spectacles."

"Can you remember if it was raining or snowing?"

"It was neither, it was eternally spring," she replied.

* * *

She remembered sitting on a sun-lounger beside a swimming pool. She wore a gold lamé one-piece swimsuit that gave the impression, was *meant* to give the impression, of freshly applied paint. Her long blonde hair was tied up in a bandana and she wore sunglasses with exaggerated white frames. On the table beside her there was a strawberry-colored cocktail in a tall glass and a box of Sobranie cigarettes and an imitation vintage copy of *Harper's Bazaar*.

Suddenly there was a small commotion. Three young men wearing swimming trunks had danced, leapt, and run across the terrace and jumped into the pool. They resurfaced, laughing and splashing the surface of the water, shaking their heads so it was like they gave off sparks. She recognized them, as much by intuition as knowledge, as members of an acrobatic dance company that was staying in the hotel. She thought, *They are the happiest people I have ever seen. It is impossible to see them without feeling happy one-self. Tonight I shall make love to all of them or none of them because to separate them would break the structure of a tableau that has taken hours of rehearsal to create.* She smiled because it was impossible not to be happy. She took a sip of the cocktail and lit a slender blue Sobranie cigarette.

* * *

She smiled at the memory. She said, "You once bought me a bouquet of flowers and in the middle of the bouquet was a rose."

"Yes, I remember."

"Oh, surely not! I've always loved the way you buy me flowers when there isn't any necessity, I mean apart from a birthday or an anniversary or even an apology. It's wonderfully *you*. But the bouquet to which I'm referring..."

"But I do remember..."

"Oh, darling, you must've bought me dozens — no, *hundreds* — of bouquets in the last ten years. I'm talking about a very *specific* bouquet. A bouquet of mixed summertime flowers in the middle of which was a single orange rose. If it had been a green rose or a blue rose..."

"It wasn't. It wasn't green or blue. It was orange."

"It was orange because I just *told* you it was orange. Oh, if I asked if you remembered, it wasn't a proper question, just a figure of speech..."

"But I *do* remember," he replied.

"What do you — no, *how* do you — remember?"

"Because the bouquet was too large to fit in a single vase, so you divided it into two. The vase containing the rose—"

"The orange rose..." she interrupted.

"—you placed on the bathroom windowsill. Our bathroom was — still is — all white: white walls, white ceiling, white sanitation chamber, white windowsill. But every day for at least a week there was this incredibly beautiful orange rose, almost like some kind of totemic sun, against this background of totalitarian — *white*. And each day, of course, it expanded, opened out, and seemed—"

"And seemed?" she again interrupted.

"—extraordinarily *excited*. For what reason, exactly, I have never known, but I don't think there has ever been — well, if not a day, at least a week — when I haven't remembered that rose and thought about it. The contrast. Not just between the rose and the bathroom, but between the rose and the bathroom and myself," he concluded.

"Now *I* remember. I used to sanitate naked and imagine my skin was becoming the petals of the rose. And when I stepped out of the sanitation chamber—"

"You believed for one moment of passionate empathy that you and the rose had become one," he noted.

"I truly believed. And when we made love, I tore you to pieces with my fingernails because my fingernails had become thorns. And when we lay apart the sweat on my skin had become the dew on the petals of a rose. And when I died on the bathroom windowsill—"

"When you died..."

"—I was reincarnated as someone the same, but *not* the same. As some new version, like a composer's variation on a theme. I cracked and peeled and flayed myself, and the sound I made was like walking over pebbles on a beach and at the same time peeling a strip of sellotape off a sheet of glass. I was realized as metal and silver and glistened like the underside of the lid on a jar of honey when the jar is new. Do you remember?"

"One cannot remember what one never knew. I remember the dead petals on the bathroom windowsill. I remember the texture of them in the palm of my hand. I remember the long lacerations and the curling wood-shavings of skin when we made love. But memory is a genie that constantly reshapes its own bottle. Indeed, I often wonder where memory ends and fiction begins..."

It had rained for nine days. The color had long ago bleached out of the world and the cupolas and the domes and the rooftops were pewter-gray. Even the sky was saturated, and it rippled in the breeze like a photograph in a developing tray. She said, "The taxi driver turned left instead of right. A blind alley. Sheets of newspaper blowing around the fire-escapes. A cat with enormous yellow eyes caught in the headlamps. A woman's scream coming from an upstairs window. A slamming casement. A sound of breaking glass."

"Where did we end up?" he asked.

"In a bar on the waterfront. In a bar that catered solely for fishermen and longshoremen and all the rough types of women that rely on both. A bar divided from the sea by an all-pervading smothering jungle of masts and spars and impenetrable fog. A bar where, when the door swung open, all the ghosts of the dead and the drowned crammed like a sickening mist through the aperture, small wisps of them, that might've been fingers or toes, trickling across the spit-stained, beer-stained wooden floor."

"I remember," he said. "I wore a white roll-necked sweater and a jacket with brass buttons. I was sitting next to a man who was drinking bourbon and smoking a marijuana cigarette. The bartender had *J E S U S* tattooed across the fingers of his right hand and *S A T A N* tattooed across the fingers of his left. I remember an atmosphere of permanent dampness and suppressed violence and hopeless grief."

"I remember the foghorn. In fact, that's *all* I remember. What are those birds that fly by night over the ocean?" she asked.

"Albatrosses?" he guessed.

"No. Well, maybe they do, but those aren't the birds I'm thinking of. I imagined I was one of those birds in silent passage over an unknown sea, guided only by a lozenge of amber-colored light shining dimly through the mist and the sound of a foghorn reminding me that I was close to land."

"Frigate birds?" he supplied.

"That's right, thank you. Frigate birds. Now I remember. They can fly for weeks, alone in the darkness of the night and then alone above an empty sunlit sea."

"There is a film where they run through The Louvre in Paris."

"There is a novel where they steal a painting called *The Rhinoceros* from The National Gallery in London."

They were silent for a moment, their soundtrack only the steady white noise of the rain. She said, "There are birds called frigate birds... What was I wearing when we first met?"

"You were wearing toreador pants and a white cotton shirt. And a pearl on a thin gold chain between the oyster of your breasts," he recalled.

"I remember now. I remember everything. I remember climbing out of a yellow taxi and entering a tall building. I remember looking up and seeing story upon story of galleries, voices echoing, and rows upon rows of expressionless faces looking down. Awful faces, disturbing faces, faces without noses or mouths or eyes, but still those voices, those echoing voices, passing some kind of judgment, issuing some kind of sentence in response to an unspecified crime."

"I remember everything too. Except what we talked about before the rain," he said.

He flicked his cigarette away and put his hand on her shoulder. The cotton of her dress was damp and revealed the strap of her brassiere. She shivered and placed her own free hand on his. She said, "Now, if there is any truth in any legend at all, the dead will arise from the sea and reclaim their presence on the land. Bedraggled and fish-blinded, trailing seaweed, their thigh-high boots oozing with—"

"Mud and foul water?"

"—and spilling shoals of whitebait from the holes that pirates made. Do you see them yet?" she asked.

"I think I do."

Together they watched the reanimated sailors of a distant past walk towards them through successive sheets of rain. The woman was strikingly beautiful and the man simultaneously elegant and handsome, and the contrast between themselves and that which approached was almost like a curtain of static electricity through which neither they nor their submarine visitors could pass. Together they watched the shades of ancient shipwrecks fade into an endless ocean of rain.

* * *

Harry sat down beside me, the gun on his lap. He said, "Hey, kiddo."

"Uh, huh."

"Nobody's breathing out here except us."

I looked along the shore and saw Billy Ray laid out on the sand, his feet facing the ocean, a bottle of beer still upright in his outstretched hand. Eight-Ball had disappeared behind a couple of old rowboats drawn up on the beach. They had been overturned and, in the uneasy half-light of early morning, resembled strange creatures washed up by a storm. I said, "I hate it when the night's over but the day won't start."

In the forty or so minutes since we drove onto the beach, the sea had changed from purple to red to an urgent cobalt blue. The sun, however, had stubbornly refused to rise and was caught between the green horizon and the orange sky like a buoy with horizontal blue and yellow stripes stuck in a slick of tar. *Or a balloon,* I thought, *with too much weight in its basket that can't get above the rooftops.* I took a pack of Luckies out of my shirt pocket and Harry took one and I took one and then Harry went around the back of the car and got us two more beers. He had a bottle-opener on his key ring. He said, "How 'bout we drive down to Slatz' Diner, get some breakfast? Bacon and eggs and home fries. Coffee and cold beer."

"Okay."

Harry handed me his beer bottle while he was reversing. He swung the wheel over and looked up in the rear-view mirror. He caught my eye. He said, "I wouldn't worry 'bout Billy Ray nor Eight-Ball."

"I wasn't."

We weren't. Harry's 1958 Thunderbird turned off the beach and back onto the road. The sky in the rear-view mirror glowed a kind of sick feverish orange. I lit a cigarette and rolled down the passenger-side window and watched the sun stuck in the ocean get smaller and smaller until it was too small to see.

VHS Memoirs

Joseph J. Dowling

I reach out from an exquisite fog, and my surroundings swim into focus. A familiar smell registers, like a hit of weak cocaine. I know the place intimately, but my jumbled memory has fragmented. Pieces float past, out of reach, then it hits me. I'm standing in my local video store — Take Two Video.

I haven't been here in over two decades, and with good reason — the store closed down at *least* twenty years ago. I look around the place, finding it exactly as I remember. My fingers run softly across the faces of the empty VHS boxes, wedged together in rows, their covers facing out. The slightly dappled surface of the vinyl and the cheap pine of the display rack feel real, unlike the absent tactility of dreams.

One other person occupies the room. A man similar in age, with lightly tanned skin and wispy, sandy-colored hair, thinning on top with a high forehead, where his hairline has receded like so many routed soldiers. He wears a friendly smile, exposing near-perfect front teeth. Hidden behind five-day ginger stubble, his face is moderately good-looking, yet forgettable, but his haunting blue eyes are sharp and alive, and they draw me in. They're a swirling cauldron of conflicting emotions, yet impossible to read.

He wears the casual uniform I remember Take Two employees always wore — black trousers, a white short-sleeved shirt and a red waistcoat, no tie — but I've not seen this man before, and I knew every employee by name. His nametag says *David*, below the embossed yellow logo in a slanted Eras Bold font, *Take Two Video*.

Despite never having worked here, I have the same uniform on. I touch the nametag pinned to my chest and lift it towards me. *Samuel.* My name.

In a soft voice, neither high-pitched nor deep, the man speaks, like a doctor talking to a patient awakening after a great trauma. "Hey Sam, how are you feeling?"

I hesitate, unsure of what to say. All I manage is, "What's happening to me?" My voice sounds strained and rough, like I've been screaming.

"It'll come to you soon enough, Sam. There's no rush," he says, returning to his task of cataloguing the stack of new arrivals sitting next to the stock computer. The ancient, flat desktop PC has a twelve-inch monochrome green monitor sitting atop its discolored plastic shell, which has turned from off-white to an almost nicotine yellow. Its old hard drive buzzes like a vitriolic autumn wasp, just as it always did.

The fog clouding my brain eases, and images of recent events slowly swirl behind my eyes. Memories of my fateful science project: the cold extraction of codeine from sixty-four co-codamol tablets, then washing down the foraged opiate with a few bottles of good red wine. I thought, *why go out drinking the cheap crap?* Afterwards, I lay on the bed and fell into gentle marshmallow oblivion. Warmth enveloped me. Worry and regret slipped away, and the infinite vantablack welcomed me in its benign embrace.

So, I must've died. Then is this purgatory? Have I been wrong all along about death being the everlasting nothingness they promised me in fantasies of motorcycle emptiness? Am I facing an inquisition to ascertain which version of the afterlife they'll eternally thrust me into?

I turn to David. "Am I dead?"

He laughs softly and shakes his head. "No, Sam, you're not dead. You're still alive, but on life support in hospital."

"So why am I here? Is it some hyper-realistic dream induced by whatever they've put in my system to chase out the opiates?"

"Long story short, you've got a decision to make. We're here until the store closes at ten tonight, after which time you can continue with your chosen path, and they pull the plug. You'll die, like you wanted to."

"And if I decide otherwise?"

"They'll do everything they can to pull you through. It's how they deal with unsuccessful suicides now. Human rights and all that. It's no longer considered ethical to *prevent* suicide, but if you fail, they're obliged to give you a chance to reconsider."

In my mind something sparks, and I recall reading a science article about some new technology for coma patients, where doctors plug them into a virtual experience to communicate with their unconscious mind.

Another, far more malignant memory blindsides me, as clear and fresh as an alpine lake under a moonless night, and every bit as dark. Waking from an entirely different opiate-induced slumber. Lauren's crumpled form next to me, purple, bruised, and distorted. After the investigation and autopsy came another crushing blow — a one-two punch which perhaps set me off to my ultimate attempt at destruction — I hadn't even known she was pregnant.

So, was that incident the catalyst for my decision, or had the path leading me to suicide begun many years before? Working it out was a knotted shoelace — unpick the wrong thread and it would tighten like a snake coiled around a struggling mouse. Choose correctly and it could unravel with ease. The shackles might finally slip off. I look at David for help. He says nothing but gives a half-smile and shrugs while I circle the store, eyeing back-to-back rows of densely packed cases arranged by genre, all spine-facing, like books. So many movies I've forgotten. Signposts of my life from childhood, through adolescence, adulthood, and finally here, at what might be its approaching end. *The Muppets, Weekend at Bernie's, Fear & Loathing In Las Vegas, Life Is Beautiful.*

The store always ran a midweek promotion, Monday through Thursday. Rent three videos and get the cheapest one for free. I sometimes took hours to peruse the store and make my selections. Perhaps I enjoyed the procrastination of choosing as much as watching. One day, as I returned three tapes in their blue hard-plastic cases, plain except for the Take Two Video sticker on the front, I found the shelves empty behind a locked door. The business had gone, vanished overnight like a guilty one-night stand.

While my doomsday clock ticks onwards, I allow my mind to wander deeper. John, the real owner of Take Two Video, with his curly hair and Magnum P.I. moustache, always took time to chat, unlike the surly younger assistant, who eyed me with indifference, or perhaps disdain. I understood why as I grew older and also despised boys that age, with their sickly-sweet smell of early pubescence, their inane interests, and weak conversation.

But John never flashed me a look of annoyance as I eulogized about some silly movie. He never projected the air of a stressed man, trying to save a failing business. Updating their vast video library with DVDs was beyond their means, while down the road, their formidable chain-store competitor owned numerous copies of the expensive major new releases on both formats. John's store usually had just one tape. If someone had already rented it, you could reserve it and they called you up when it came back. After the store closed, I never saw John again.

Suddenly enraged, I spit, "So who the fuck are you then?" I want to grab David by the collar and force answers out of him one by one.

David remains unflustered as he says, "I'm you, Sam. Or at least I'm a representation of parts of you. Think of me as a devil's advocate. I'm who your mind considered most appropriate to explore existential and philosophical notions with. To help you make your decision."

I chew on this for a moment, calming down from my brief outburst. "Right, so can I ask you anything I like?"

"You can, but I only know what you know, although the subconscious is powerful. You know much more than you realize."

"OK, so why the damn video store? I haven't been here since I was a kid."

"You know why."

I search for reasons. The time has come for honesty. "I suppose this was the last place I felt truly happy, wasn't it? I always felt calm and in control here. It was my sanctuary, I guess."

Well, at least it had been until I hit my teenage years and discovered alcohol, then drugs. Good friends who became bad friends destroyed my fragile fledgling confidence, punishing me for being too weak to leave the group. Clouded by irreconcilable rage, I became a frustrated spinning top of kinetic energy, careering off in the wrong direction.

At that moment, the store's speaker system pipes out a familiar song. Even in the darkest times, I always had music. Eventually, I discovered a tribe of like-minded souls to share it with and I want to hear that playlist of my youth one final time — Pixies, Smashing Pumpkins, Green Day, Nirvana, Pearl Jam, Alice in Chains.

"Excellent choice," says David, nodding along with the rhythm. "Yes, you are right about this place. It's where your mind chose to have this discussion with itself."

I stare around, as if seeing the room for the first time. Despite the weird circumstances, it's nice to return here, with its indescribable smell, one so unique to this place I never found it anywhere else. Not good, not bad, it just *was.*

It's time to stop skirting around the fluff. I'm not here for a pleasant nostalgia trip. If I've left the building, I better exit knowing why. I force myself into the rusty and unforgiving embrace of hard memories, all the way back to my first relationship, if you could call it that, aged seventeen. Brief and intense, I pushed her away with my neediness. At least I'd lost the stink of my virginity, but what had I really learned? I expected to reach the solution slowly as I aged, like an Ice Breaker forging through frozen seas. But women are still a Rubik's cube; a cryptic puzzle which I'll never solve now.

My last relationship was messy and self-destructive. Co-dependent and co-joined, two addicts on a path of mutually-assured destruction. My poison was painkillers and opiates, hers was coke; we shared alcohol like the child of estranged parents.

So, what about *my* parents? My father — an overbearing Irish Catholic — instilled a dark shadow into my psyche. Perhaps the chains which prevent me from finding freedom all lead back to this, the source of my guilt.

His funeral was a dismal affair, just a handful of mourners in attendance and a budget service with a cheap pine coffin. The wake, held in a dingy pub, was mostly dry. Several people from his AA circle and a couple of teetotal family members comprised most of the group. One man was drinking. Aged eleven and keen to grow up, I asked him how the fizzy amber liquid tasted.

"Like camel's piss, son," he replied. How I grew to love that taste, or at least how it made me feel.

My mother was kind, but passive and ill-equipped to deal with life's complexity. We got on fine when I was younger, but as I grew, we butted heads. How much control could she exert over a nihilistic, lazy, and frustrated teenager? Our relationship improved after I left home at eighteen.

She apologized constantly. Why did she carry such a heavy burden of guilt? She did her best, but I hadn't told her I loved her since I was nine or ten. Did she die wondering? I never gave her what she needed most of all — my time. I continue through the memory hole to another funeral, the time where her burden passed on to me, her only child.

"Sorry mum," I whispered as another coffin ambled into the furnace. Gentle hands touched my shoulder as I delivered a eulogy, but in my mind were selfish thoughts about having new excuses to wallow and self-destruct.

My thoughts are getting too intense and I need a break, so I lean against the white wooden counter, my hands framing my chin like Charlie Brown.

"What do you think about how our life panned out, Dave?"

"I think you never really gave life a chance to find you. But it's never too late," he replies.

"Never too late? That's the biggest cliché of them all, isn't it?"

"Pictures of You" by the Cure plays softly in the background. The soundtrack has moved onto music I discovered later in life. We've dealt with teenage angst, for now.

"Often, the clichés are clichés for a reason. There's truth in them."

"I guess so. Should I have sobered up then? Gone into the damn program like another lost disciple, looking for something to seize control of life where I failed?"

"It may've helped, but you'll never know. Unless you choose to live, of course. But the program isn't the only option, is it?"

"I suppose not." Many people I've known down the years achieved sobriety, some in self-help groups, some via therapy or plain old-fashioned will-power. For me, it was always tomorrow. Now I have no tomorrow, only today, and not much remains of that.

"Is it just you and me here, Davey boy?"

"For now," he says. "When you're ready, we'll welcome some customers."

"I think I *am* ready."

"If you say so," he says. I look at him with a frown. I hate that passive aggressive phrase. Of course, if David shares my mind, then he knows I hate it. *Am* I ready for who might come reeling through the door?

"OK, maybe we'll wait. No rush after all, it's only six pm. Not like it's my last day on earth or anything." I drum the counter and turn away, walking over to the new releases section. So many movies to see, so little time. I've never seen *Eraserhead* or *Seven Samurai*, and now I never will. Film and music are the two things that stayed with me like loyal and valiant, but ultimately impotent, knights on horseback. Sancho P to my Don Q. There are limits to what they can do against my incompetence.

What about the path I chose? Ultimately, I failed to achieve what I believed to be my destiny. Early in my musical career, I remember meeting these bitter and resentful thirty-somethings — usually promoters or operating the sound desk. Unable to reconcile myself with failure, I unwittingly became one of them. But I had other interests, and time remained on my side. Not anymore. The sand in my personal timer has all slipped through.

"Why did we never start writing again?" I say. It was a passion once, although, like music, perhaps I overestimated my skill. Even so, it had represented an outlet, an untapped resource to live beyond the walls of fragile day-to-day existence.

"Good question. I guess we feared another failure. If you don't play, then you can't lose, right?"

I nod in agreement with myself. "It seems silly now, doesn't it? Now we're basically dead. How could we have been scared to *try*? So what if no one else cared?" Frustration rises in me.

"I think we should let some people into the store," says David, changing the subject as my anger threatens to cloud me.

"Sure, why not?" But a man already stands with his back to me, browsing the shelves. I recognize his gait. It's my father, dead for thirty years at least. His was a steep decline into sickness and senility after years of self-abuse. But this is not the pale, sickly, demented man I last knew. As he turns around, I realize he's closer to my age. Behind his thick-rimmed spectacles, fierce, intelligent hazel-colored eyes pierce mine.

"Hello lad," he says in his soft Dublin accent, diluted by decades of living in England. "You should live while you can, son. Death is deathly dull, take it from me." Stunned by this odd apparition, I grapple in vain for a response. "I weighed you down with guilt, and I'm sorry. You know us Catholics, always passing it on like some hallowed artifact. Forcing regurgitated nonsense about sex being sinful down the throats of our offspring, like chewed up worms to a baby bird." Still, I say nothing as he continues. "I can't stay, but I just wanted you to know I'm sorry." He turns to David and places his selection on the counter. A porno movie — tame by modern standards, no doubt.

"Two pounds please," David says. My father fumbles inside his tweed jacket and fishes out a crumpled old blue five-pound note, long since out of circulation. David passes back three chunky old pounds.

He turns to me. His fingers rise quickly towards the side of my head and he snaps them back. His palm opens, revealing a coin — not the common quid, but an ornate silver coin I don't recognize. Beneath a portrait of me, in profile like some kind of monarch, the year of my birth is etched: 1983.

"You'll have potatoes growing soon if you don't wash behind those ears," he says, before striding out of Take Two Video. I haven't said a word. I want to say *something* to him, at least.

"What happens if I leave the store?"

"Try it and see," David replies.

I follow my father and catch the door as it closes, yanking it back open. But I can't move beyond its threshold, stuck like a fly in a jar. What did I expect? I've been finding ways to trap myself since I learned how to construct cages of my own.

David splutters at me, "They always try that."

"That was a barrel of laughs. What's next, some uncle I'd forgotten used to molest me?"

"Let's deal with both parents first."

My mother shuffles through the door, smiling warmly as she recognizes me.

"Sammy, I know you don't have much time. I always take up too much of your precious time as it is."

"Mum, I..." my voice trails off as I grasp for the words.

She stops and looks at me, full of expectation. "Yes, son?"

"You... you know I love you, right? I'm sorry for giving you such a hard time back then, and being such a selfish shit. I don't blame you for anything." Tears prick at my eyes, but I won't let them come. I never let them come.

"I didn't." She pauses. "But I do now. That's all I needed to hear. Good luck with it all. See you *not* soon, I hope." She turns and leaves. She didn't get more than a few feet inside the store.

"What now?"

David offers, "What about one of your teachers? Maybe you'd like to speak to one of them?"

Two people come to mind from high school, for opposite reasons. One, my music teacher, is somebody I want to tell how much I despise his guts. How much his words of discouragement hurt me, and what a spiteful piece of shit I believe he is. The other, my math teacher, went out of her way, putting in extra hours to help me through my exam.

"But which?"

"What good would the former serve you now?" He's right. My math teacher, Mrs. Blake enters, with her plain-but-kind face.

She says, "I'm disappointed with how it's worked out for you, Samuel, but I've always had faith in you. I know you can turn it around." But can I?

"Thank you. It meant a lot to me how much you helped me back then. Without you, I'd never have scraped a pass. Not that it matters much now, I guess."

Next, I meet Briony and Caroline, two of the greatest hits from my back catalogue of unsuccessful relationships. My inability to put anyone first but myself resonates, familiar echoes of the same behavior which drove them away.

Then, Daniel enters. We've known each other since primary school. Sometimes Daniel was my worst tormentor, other times a confidant. In the end, I hated him, but how could an only child relate to the thick skin a younger sibling needs? I remember the disdain with which Rick, his surly and mean older brother, always looked at me. To both boys, I came across as weak. Weakness had to be confronted.

"I tried to toughen you up, Sam. Look at it like that. Some of the others were just pricks, but then if you walked a mile in their shoes, you'd understand."

So, it was never about me, but I presented an easy target on which to exorcise frustration. Projection, I believe they call it now.

"I think I've had enough ghosts for one day," I announce, suddenly exhausted.

But David's tall forehead creases and his arms fold. "Sorry, Samuel, there's one more. It won't be much fun either." His eyes dart to the space over my shoulder.

Lauren was my partner for a couple of years in my early thirties, shortly after my mother's death. We met as two kindred spirits, finding each other in the darkness — her, a childhood survivor of sexual abuse, me lonely and lost. I introduced her to the ephemeral release of opiate high, but she proved a far better student, breaking through my glass ceiling and onto the next level. I didn't keep my side of the deal, though, and her thin armor buckled.

I turn and she's facing me. Her translucent white skin shines in the light, her green eyes haunted by things I can never know. Did I think I could skip this?

"Don't say you've forgotten me?" she says. How could I have? She died with my unborn child still inside her.

"No, I—"

"Save it. You're alive, we're dead. Consider it a gift and forgive yourself, because no one else can do it for you." Then she fades away, leaving nothing but shelves full of videotapes.

"So, what do we do now?" I say to David, as the clock ticks inexorably forward. "Are you going to show me our future like some kind of Dickensian trope?"

"You know there's no such thing as time travel. But you have given me an idea." He pulls out a video from the middle of the stack of new arrivals and unsheathes it from its glossy case, before ejecting a cassette from the combination TV/VHS recorder mounted to the wall above. He replaces it with his tape.

"Looks like it might be worth a watch, don't you think?" he says as he snaps the empty box closed and passes it across for me to examine. *What next for Sam?* It looks like a spoof movie, with an actor who looks like me adorning the cover. He's more handsome, with a strong jawline instead of my round face, and a perfect widow's peak in place of the jagged Mediterranean hairline bequeathed to me from an unknown lineage.

We watch the tape. It runs more like a montage of scenes and vignettes than a cohesive film. Sure, it might not win any Oscars, but it isn't bad, in that nothing-much-happens, mumble-core way.

"Wouldn't you rather live that life instead of nothing at all?" says David.

"Yeah, I guess, but surely the film represented only an idea of what *could* happen. Like you say, we can't know the future, any more than we can change the past."

"Wouldn't you prefer to find out?"

David has a point. The clock on the wall ticks to 9:55 pm—nearly closing time. We stand frozen for another minute, unable to hold each other's gaze.

"Time's almost up, Sam, old friend. I need to ask you the question." David pauses. Our stares finally lock and can no longer be broken. "What's it going to be?"

I still haven't decided. But not choosing means choosing to die. An idea flashes into my head and I smile. Clasped in my slick palm, I've kept the silver coin my father gave me.

I examine David, the person my own psyche has created, as I say, "Why don't we toss for it?" My hand unfurls and I examine the coin's reverse side, discovering an engraving of a raven above an incomplete inscription. Twenty-something, the year of my death, still to be determined. My smile becomes a grin. "Heads or tails?"

As if speaking to a slow schoolboy who doesn't quite understand, he says carefully, "Heads for life, tails for death. That's pretty obvious, isn't it?"

"Yes, I suppose it is, good buddy." Without further theatre, I flip the coin. It spins straight and true, end-over-end countless times, until it reaches its inevitable apex, where gravity must reclaim it like melting ice in a glass of water on a hot day. Time slows as its descent begins. I try to follow as it continues spinning endlessly. Heads, tails, heads, tails, my life reduced to a game show and a decelerating wheel of fortune.

Click.clack.click.clack.click.clack..click..clack...click...clack....click....

The coin lands perfectly in the center of my open palm. I slam it onto the back of my other hand and look up at David. His gaze is fixed on my hairy-knuckled paw.

"Ready?" I ask. He says nothing and his eyes flick up to my face before returning to the hand covering the coin. I pull it away to reveal tails. *Death.*

An electric chill travels down my spine and I finally know what I want, more than I've ever desired anything. More than I coveted that bright yellow toy truck in the shop window when I was five. More than I ached to follow in the footsteps of my rock-star idols from the nineties. A famous closing soliloquy from a movie I once loved plays through my head, distorting as it becomes the final scene in the film of my life so far. But will there be a sequel?

"I choose... I choose *life!*"

Beastly

Christopher Hadin

The field was mostly brown now. A few green leaves remained, low on the tough, woody stems of weeds, but these too were showing hints of yellow in the damp November air. Carl Morgan parked his station wagon and walked past the plexiglass map at the edge of the parking lot. The Eagle Scout that made it had put a covered wooden box to hold trail maps, but once the maps had all been taken, no one printed any more. Then someone had crammed the box full of bagged dog droppings and the box began to rot from the inside out.

Carl had come here nearly every day for fifteen years. It was Monty's favorite place. As a young dog, Monty had menaced the wildlife of the preserve, bounding through the brush, putting birds to flight and frightening rabbits back down their holes. Then canine middle age set in and he preferred the trail.

But even now with Monty's ashes in an urn on the mantle, Carl was occasionally drawn to the preserve for walks across the field and the pathways beside the stream. Thousands of walks on these trails allowed his mind's eye to overlap with the scenery before him, and he could half-see Monty beside him. As the years progressed, the dog went from jumping over logs on the trail, to climbing over until finally, as his hind legs stiffened, he needed to be lifted over each obstruction, then put down gently on the other side. Carl could still see it. The memory of lifting Monty over fallen logs was as much in his arms and back as it was in his mind. At each log, he remembered how it felt to pause and bend over, and how Monty had lowered his haunches, allowing himself to be scooped up.

Earlier in the spring, someone went through the preserve with a bow saw and cut out sections of the logs that had lain across the trail for years, allowing little geriatric dogs to pass with ease. It was a sign of how blind Monty had become when he stopped at these points along the now-cleared trail, waiting to be lifted over logs that were no longer there. Carl had tried to show him that he was now free to walk the trail unencumbered. But Monty couldn't see that there were no longer barriers in front of him, nor could he hear Carl urging him on. In his prime, the dog had known hundreds of human words, or seemed to at least, responding to and executing complex two-part commands. Except for the sense of smell, it was doubtful he had any senses left to negotiate his world.

On the day in mid-September that Monty did not go stand by the door, Carl did not take him. It was clear that he had stopped enjoying his daily walks, and only participated out of habit. Carl carried him to the back yard where he dutifully completed his business and then stood, as though before a log, waiting for Carl to pick him up and carry him inside to his bed. A few days later, he died quietly in his sleep.

Since then, Carl's visits to the preserve were irregular. He had spent most of his time in the house, doing nothing for exercise, and he quickly put on ten pounds. This weight gain was noticed by his doctor. "You need to get back out there. Get another dog. Adopt one, and if you don't want to do that, you need to take yourself for walks. Take yourself out. You gotta attend to your own care and feeding. Ever read those James Herriot books?"

"My daughter did."

"Herriot advised against a mourning period. Your little fellow's memory won't be tarnished by going over to the shelter this afternoon and seeing what they have." Carl nodded without much conviction while his doctor scribbled on a pad. "Here you go." He handed over a prescription. "Take this to the shelter and have them fill it." Carl took out his glasses and read: "Canine accompaniment for 1 hour walk, 2X daily."

Carl chuckled and put the paper in his pocket. "Okay, I'll think about it."

"Walk while you think. Those ten pounds need to come off. Then another ten."

And so, on a dreary morning in November, he finished his coffee and by a force of will, made his hand go to the back of the door, take his coat off a hook and put it on. He was directing himself in a detached way, taking his animal body for a walk as instructed. Perhaps a dog would come later. It was difficult enough to get his bipedal mammalian self to do what he told it to do.

At the preserve, Carl walked through the field, noting the persistence of asters and other scrubby little blossoms where only a few months before, Queen Anne's lace had reigned amid black-eyed Susan and bee balm. Now their stalks were dead, the dried flowers spilling tiny seeds into the wind.

The path entered the woods. It led to a stream where old farm roads had once met, crossing the water in the distant, rural past. When Monty was alive, Carl tended to avoid these old roads with their stone walls and rows of sugar maples. They were frequented by phone-engrossed people who walked their dogs off-leash, staring at their screens, unmindful. Interactions with the dogs of road walkers often led to aggression, which Carl noted was never initiated by Monty, but, in the manner characteristic of his breed, he never backed down from a good fight either. Because of this, Carl and Monty always walked the rarely used trails that skirted the edge of the ravine, where the stream was ten to twenty feet or so below the forest floor.

While walking along an unusually high side of the ravine, where the stream had cut deeply into a small hill, Carl came upon an odd construction of logs and branches. At first, he thought someone had made a fence across the trail, but when he got closer, he saw that there were actually two parallel fences, perpendicular to the trail and the edge of the ravine. The two fences formed a kind of chute, instantly calling to mind the fences of a stockyard, where cattle were driven onward to the knives and cleavers that turned them to steaks, roasts and burgers.

The fences were woven with deadfall from the surrounding trees and must have taken someone several hours to construct. He reached out and tried to give one of them a shake, but it was surprisingly solid and resisting. Someone had been very determined, but to what purpose? Carl was wondering what Monty would have made of it when he looked down and saw a series of deliberate scratches in an exposed slab of rock. He realized it was lettering, a small, very crudely gouged sign that said: "this way ↑." It was meant to be read from the mouth of the chute and it pointed to the edge of the ravine. Carl stepped back and took in the scene. The fences were there to guide victims to over the edge of the ravine where they would haplessly fall onto the rocks below.

"Boys," he said aloud. Only boys would be able to marshal the energy needed to collect all the deadfall and construct the crude fences in the naive hope of causing someone to fall into the water. Only boys, with their morbid fascinations and malicious instincts, would devise such a trap and, in the absence of proper signage, sit down, rock-to-rock, and scratch out letters urging the witless on to their doom.

Of course, the trap would catch no one. It was all an elaborate game. Few visitors to the preserve looked up from their phones long enough to know that the ravine side trails even existed, even though, as Carl liked to think, these trails probably predated the coming of Europeans by hundreds or perhaps thousands of years. They were no doubt ancient, these footpaths along the ravine, like trails alongside rivers all over the world. "The land is timeless," he whispered to himself. He felt, for just a moment, an expanse of time where the coming of fields and paved roads and ranch houses was merely a blip in a vast continuum. He forgot where he was for a second.

He looked back down at the fences and wondered how many boys had worked on the project. Probably six or seven he reasoned, since the energy required to gather that much wood would have exhausted the attention of one or two of them. No, it was probably more.

He smiled as he pictured how it would have gone. The idea would have formed with one or two ringleaders and the reason for it would have been self-evident — to get people to fall off into the ravine. He had undertaken similar projects when he was nine or ten — clever contrivances designed to make girls trip and fall down. He could imagine them working together. "Guys! Guys!" one boy would say. "Guys! We need more wood!" The ringleader would of course be the taskmaster. "Come on! We gotta make this fence and get someone to fall!" Perhaps the second in command would announce that they needed a sign, and he would have looked around for a rock to scratch out letters in the soft, crumbly schist. Looking back in the woods, Carl saw piles of leaves that had been scuffed off the forest floor. A series of unmistakable arrows pointing to the chute had been swept into a pathway, most likely with their feet, kicking away the leaves down to the bare soil.

It was a wonder kids still did things like this since he never saw children playing outside. They all had phones. Even the little ones, and that's what they all did now — they sat around and looked at screens. Swiping left or right. They never looked where they were. Never watched where they were going. But apparently there were still a few primal instincts left in children. Outside of the doting supervision that was now commonplace, boys still returned to their malevolent destructive instincts. It pleased him that when unsupervised, children still had imaginations.

"Perfectly beastly!" Carl looked across the ravine to see a woman speaking to him with a clipped British accent, high and shrill. She was old and her white hair hung in a neatly trimmed pageboy. She wore a gray cardigan with chunky wooden buttons. It was trimmed with embroidered flowers and symbols that Carl did not recognize. A long, somewhat dingy, denim skirt went down below the tops of her yellow rain boots.

"Nearly ten of them and they were perfectly beastly!"

Carl laughed. "I imagine they were. I almost fell victim to their trap," he joked.

"Well you're lucky you had your wits about you or you'd have been dashed to pieces on the stones of perdition."

Carl heard himself laughing again, as though from a few feet away. "I didn't know children still played like this — without screens to tell them what to do or how to do it."

"Indeed. The technological revolution has done little to abate the destructive hearts of ten-year-old boys," she said, nodding appreciatively.

"I was the same I suppose." Carl started to mention his device to make girls trip and fall, but decided against it. "With luck most of us grow out of it."

"More's the pity!" She shook her head with regret. "Because for the world to turn and for society to function you must have tribes of perfectly beastly little boys. They must be utterly monstrous in their lawlessness!"

"Well I suppose that is the natural order of things," Carl said, trying to normalize the conversation that was beginning to take a very odd turn.

"And you must have legions of mercilessly cruel little girls. Legions of them!"

Carl said nothing this time. The woman stared at him as a faint smile spread over her face. Her eyes were dark behind the thick lenses that distorted the top half of her head, making it appear to narrow at the eyes. *The better for her to see you with,* he thought.

"These are the only children who will become men and women capable of doing what's needed in this world. The old gods depend on it!" she said, her voice loud and shrill.

Carl nodded vaguely. He looked away. "Well, enjoy your walk," he said, not wanting to invite any more of her philosophy of child development. She did not return his pleasantry, and when he glanced back, she was standing where he had first seen her. She seemed to have no intention of leaving.

* * *

It was later during a damp week that Carl forced himself into his raincoat and drove slowly to the preserve. The days were getting shorter, and he struggled to fill the hours. And so many things were a dead end. So many full stops with no logical flow into something else. He needed to box up more of Carol's clothes for Goodwill, but each outfit triggered a memory and each memory opened the door to grief. Too many times he found himself sitting in a darkened room, a blouse of Carol's in his hands or folded in his lap, not knowing when it had gotten dark or for how long it had been so. He was often frozen in place in the rooms of his house, with no comfortable past to return to and no future to anticipate. There was only this static present. His chest ached, but it was from holding his breath. In the still, quiet rooms he found that he breathed only enough to keep himself alive, each breath held, then released. Each inhalation taken only when its need was acute.

In these moments he had learned to put on his coat and go to the preserve. He reached for Monty's leash which hung from a hook behind the door, but pulled his hand back. Touching the braided leather evoked the world of sense memory; it brought back the feeling of Monty's compact little torso, the wobble of his left ear as he trotted along; the stub of a tail, wagging faster than the human eye could register.

At the preserve he parked his car, stepped out, and had a strong sensation of being untethered, as though he bobbed on the surface of the world, oddly unencumbered — but not from happiness. It was a loose, reckless feeling that he fought back by taking slow, deliberate steps. It seemed that Monty was there, just not visible. Carl was aware of the physical space that the little dog had once occupied, and this space seemed to have a density that affected the dull gray daylight, bending it in on itself so that the shape of the dog was made all the more visible. When he looked, deliberately trying to see it, there was nothing to see.

Carl was considering reasons for this sensation when he looked up to see a boy on a bicycle, bearing down on him. He stepped quickly to the side as the boy darted past, missing him, but just barely. There was no doubt the boy had intentionally steered as close to him as possible. Carl turned to watch him cross the field. The boy had a weird way of riding his bike, staring at the forks, head down, not looking where he was going. He seemed to navigate the bumpy pathway across the field with a sense other than sight as he slipped between the boulders at the edge of the parking lot and was gone.

Carl looked back and saw movement through the trees. A group of boys on bikes came out of the opening to the woods and entered the narrow pathway through the field. This time, Carl stepped back into the weeds and watched them approach. They stood on the pedals, swaying their bikes side to side with a strange unity of motion. Like a school of fish or a flock of starlings, they maintained an even space between, each functioning as the whole with no apparent direction. Like the first boy, they stared at the ground in front of them, moving across the field and navigating the uneven ground in a tight group, not strung out as he would have expected them to be with strong riders outpacing the slower ones and a straggler or two bringing up the rear. He took another step backwards as they passed in silence. They were like the bike-riding automatons he saw perched above the funhouse at the Catholic school's annual carnival — torsos rigid, the turning pedals moving the riders' legs in synchronized rotations.

Carl watched them slip between the boulders at the edge of the parking lot and disappear from sight behind the trees. He stepped back onto the trail and looked down. One of them had dropped a small, crudely-made doll, sewn together with coarse, uneven stitches. It was a man in a long blue coat and khaki pants. It had no face or hands. Carl held it for a few moments before seeing that the blue fabric of the doll's coat was nearly identical to his own. The pants were not as close a match, but were, nevertheless, khaki in color. "This could be me," he said aloud. A bit of twine tied around the figure's middle was like a belt, giving the impression of a medieval tunic. The twine was tied to something in the grass and when he pulled it up to his hands, he saw the thing was a tightly felted ball of wool, mixed with strands of red hair, shiny and fine. The ball had four little twists that stuck out like legs. A little felt Monty.

It was at the moment when he realized the doll in his hand might not be a complete coincidence, Carl looked up to the high edge of the hillside meadow and saw the woman he'd talked to a few days ago. She held her hands in the cavernous kangaroo pocket of a rough wool anorak and looked down on him with benign interest, though she did not smile. He waved but she did not wave back. He held up the doll, pointing at it and shrugging as if to say, *Can you believe this?* Carl laughed a little, anticipating that there would be some reaction from the woman but there was none. She continued staring down on him from the high edge of the meadow where there was no trail. Her face had no look of recognition or emotion. She might as well have been watching a cloud.

He stared back at her and saw that her mouth was moving, but he couldn't hear any words. She didn't seem to be speaking to him but rather, staring at him while repeating the same words over and over. Her gaze gradually left him and rose to a point above the trees on the opposite side of the field. He couldn't be certain but he thought her lips formed the words "perfectly beastly" six times before they once again returned to their neutral set. He put the doll in his pocket, along with the little ball of wool and hair, and walked to his car. At the edge of the field, he turned back to see if she was still watching him, but she was gone.

Later, Carl sat at his kitchen table, staring at the doll's head. On closer examination, it did have an odd little face, if two dots from a ballpoint pen counted for eyes and a faint straight line for a mouth. He noticed that the dog had light brown patches across its hind end like Monty, before the years faded the caramel-colored markings that he sported as a younger dog. The oblong ball of wool and red hair also had two spots for eyes and a black spot for a nose. It was a crude but effective likeness.

Carl thought hard, trying to remember if he had ever encountered kids on bikes at the preserve, but he couldn't; not one single time out of the thousands of walks he'd taken there. And the woman with the enthusiasm for feral children — he'd never seen her there before either. He thought of how he'd encountered her today, moments after seeing the boys and how her observant but disinterested face looked on him like a fixture of the landscape, his wave *hello* like the flutter of leaves in the breeze, random and meaningless. He had been observed but not seen, or perhaps she had seen through him to something else, like one looks through the fog that lingers after dawn. Like a predator looks at prey, or a cattleman looks at his herd, seeing only meat on the hoof. *What are the words for a human face, empty of all human emotion?* Carl wondered, He decided it didn't matter.

Staring at the doll, Carl began to doubt it was meant for him to see. What purpose would that serve? What meaning would be conveyed? He decided to put it on one of the fences by the ravine where the boy who made it would find it. But then, what message would that convey? He didn't know, but it seemed like an appropriate course of action, perhaps a way of saying, *I'm watching you watching me.* He noticed this morning that the stuffing was coming through a small slit on the front of the coat, something he didn't see when he had studied it in the field. They would be sorry to have lost it, and happy to have it back. He'd take it tomorrow, but until then the little representation of himself and Monty would have to stand against the salt and pepper shakers, watching over the table until morning.

It rained heavily all night, but the rain had stopped by the time Carl got up for his coffee. Little Carl and Monty were still there against the salt and pepper. The weather made him stiff and he moved slowly, transferring his coffee to a travel mug. "Are you ready?" he said to his little self, pausing long enough for a reply. "Well okay. Let's go." He put them in his pocket, turned off the light, and flicked the lock on the door knob. He never used the dead-bolt anymore. It seemed a wasted effort to secure this house. What would

anyone want to take? Outside, the smell of damp fallen cottonwood leaves was thick in the air. It was almost warm.

Carl parked and took a path through the woods, skipping the field. The wooded trail would take him more directly to the place high above the stream where the boys had constructed their trap. It followed one of the old cart paths that was deeply cut into the hillside between stone walls that were above eye level of a passerby. It was one of the straighter sections of trail, lined with venerable sugar maples and wide-branching white oaks, but because of its incline, it tended to wash out in heavy rain. He followed it over a small, broad hill then down to where the two fences formed the human trap on the high bank above the stream.

There had been activity. The leaves had been kicked aside, creating a longer, bare-dirt pathway from the main trail to the edge. He went down the path they had made, wondering if this was what the boys had in mind — a smooth walkway for hapless victims, who, by the time they realized they had made a mistake, could not turn back. They would be trapped with no way to go except forward over the edge. He laughed at the naivety that would have even considered such an unlikely outcome.

Carl stepped between fences, reached into his pocket for little Carl and Monty, and placed them on a log, standing together, the leash dangling. He stepped forward and peered down at the streambed, more than a dozen feet below. The boys had picked a good spot for their game. The fences were placed above a bend where, over time, the flow of water had washed away all but the larger boulders. *It would be a bone-jarring drop, that's for sure,* Carl thought to himself. *Perhaps even fatal, depending on how you fell.* He looked across the ravine at a well-worn footpath that skirted the edge and descended to the streambed. It was where he first saw the woman. For all he knew, she was the trail's sole user. In fifteen years, she was the only person he had ever seen there.

Carl turned to walk back to his car and stopped short. A boy, about ten or eleven years old, stood between the fences, blocking his exit. He held a long, straight spear, tipped with a shiny, black stone point. White lines had been painted below each of his eyes. He wore a look of intense focus. The boy shuffled forward a couple of feet, bringing the spear point closer to Carl's face. Carl could see an iridescent sheen on the edges of the point. He took a deep breath and let it out.

"Whoa. That's obsidian, buddy," he said to the boy in a friendly, conversational tone. "It's really, really sharp." The boy stood motionless, his eyes locked on Carl's face. "You built some nice fences. They're really sturdy. Nice job." The boy remained still, crouched forward, holding the spear point up to Carl's neck. He rolled the spear a little, allowing Carl to see how it was flaked on both edges. As fast as he could, Carl reached up to grab the shaft of the spear. The boy, with only the slightest flick of his wrists, jerked the spear away from Carl's grasping hand and in the same motion, drew the point across Carl's left cheek. Blood began to ooze immediately. He touched his cheek then pulled his hand away and looked at it.

"You goddamn little bastard, that's enough. I'm not playing here. Give that to me now!" He reached out to take the spear, this time not relying on quickness but on the no-nonsense authority that came with being an adult. Again, the boy flicked the tip and deftly cut a deep gash across Carl's palm, then brought the tip to rest against the knob of his throat. The boy very slowly began to increase the pressure.

Carl backed up a step and the boy advanced, keeping the pressure steady. The blood from his cheek flowed down over his chin and the gash on his hand dripped with an audible *pfit, pfit, pfit*, onto the ground. He stepped back toward the edge of the ravine. It was not a fatal drop if one went feet first and had a lucky landing. The boy's expression never changed. He pulled the spear away from Carl's throat and moved it in a sideways figure eight in front of Carl's eyes.

In one motion, Carl knocked the spear up away from his face, turned, and stepped off the bank. As he dropped, he saw another boy rush in and put an obsidian-tipped spear under him. Carl tried to knock it aside but the swipe of his arm threw him off balance and he fell sideways, the spear entering his armpit and bursting through his shoulder blade with an audible crunch. It exited his back, skewering him halfway on the shaft. He landed on his side in the shallow, rushing water of the previous night's rain. Carl's field of vision instantly went black, but the cold water and excruciating pain in his side forced his eyes wide open. He began to see blobs of sight returning — branches of trees and the gray sky beyond.

"Christ!" he called out, gasping. "Oh Christ!"

Above him on the high bank, the boy looked down without malice or aggression. His face bore no sign of curiosity or interest; it had no expression at all. The boy in the streambed backed up and turned to look at the opposite bank of the ravine. The woman was there, standing on the edge-skirting trail in the exact place he had first seen her days ago.

Carl's eyes went there too. "Help me, please," he called to her. He gasped in pain as he tried to prop himself up. "These kids have... God! They've stabbed me!"

Her expression did not change. There was no flash of alarm or urgency to rush to his aid. She stood, motionless, hands in the kangaroo pouch of her tattered anorak.

"Please, I need help," he croaked out in a soft bubbly voice, struggling to speak. "They stabbed me."

She descended into the ravine without looking, her feet finding the ancient stepping places. Slowly, she approached him, her dark eyes fixed on his own.

"Please help..." he whispered. She stood near the boy and only then did a faint, sad smile come over her. It was not a smile of compassion or empathy, but the way one smiles in the face of something that is inevitable. She motioned the boy closer to her and handed him something. When he turned, Carl saw that the boy held a sheath from which he drew an obsidian knife, blackish-gray and translucent, a molecular-fine edge to the blade.

"They have been rather beastly I'm afraid," she said. Carl tried to put out his hand. He tried to say no to the boy with the knife. "It's rather beastly work." The woman looked up to the naked branches against the sky. "Beastly work for beastly little hands."

The boy bent over Carl.

The woman closed her eyes and smiled.

On the Boardwalk

Richard Risemberg

It was the sort of day that brings people to Los Angeles, thinking they'll start over again in a new and freer life — and we were in the sort of dump they end up in, if they're not careful. A warm day in February, sitting at the outdoor tables of a sandwich stand on the Venice Beach Boardwalk, with the ocean a blue bulge in the west.

"Look at this place," Rod said. "A boardwalk with no boards. It's just an asphalt street! Why call it a 'boardwalk,' anyway?"

Rod was my work buddy; we had a little landscape job at a house just off the beach, planting what the owner called her "victory garden," like it was World War Two and she might starve if she didn't hire us to grub in her dirt. And Rod was right: the Boardwalk was just a stretch of asphalt between bright sand on one side and dreary, old apartment hotels on the other. The hotels crowded rows of souvenir shops and marijuana dispensaries into the ground floor storefronts, but upstairs they were the kind of places where old drunks go to die. Maybe that was part of the glamour of the Boardwalk; the tourists could pretend they were slumming somewhere bohemian and a little dangerous, but with good weather and the beach, and free entertainment mocking the freaks. There was no motor traffic, at least, except for the police cars creeping by with snakelike deliberation. No one on the boardwalk liked the cops, least of all the street merchants lined up on the beach side of the strip, slouched in sagging chairs with their backs to the sand, hawking bad paintings and clumsy handmade jewelry, or telling fortunes, or moaning songs to the jangle of out-of-tune guitars. The indoor shopkeepers hated the street merchants, the street merchants hated the indoor shopkeepers, and the cops hated everybody and wished they were someplace else. The eateries at least made out fine, feeding everybody, or at least everybody who had money.

So I was sitting at a cheap tin table with a plastic basket of what were alleged to be french fries in front of me, and Rod across from me with his own plastic basket where a burger awaited its fate. It was lunch time, and what better place to spend it than in this dented paradise that the world flocked to visit, at the edge of the continent, with the blue Pacific watching from a distance, hoarding its storms and tidal waves till the mood should strike it to wipe us all out.

We were watching the parade of freaks and tourists while we ate — what Rod called the "floor show," by which he specifically meant pretty women showing skin. The local phonies, poseurs, and lost souls were trying their hardest to *epater les bourgeois*, and the bourgeois were doing their best to cut loose and fit in, despite their clean clothes, tidy haircuts, and sunburned boobs. They tried hard, all right, the men showing pale knobby legs in baggy shorts, the women flaunting cleavages they would never have approved of in someone else back home, the children sneering at the hairy half-naked locals with their cancerous tans.

"The sad thing is," Rod said, "that damn near everybody here sees this place as the apotheosis of civilization. And sometimes I think they're right."

"There's plenty of people that hate this place," I said.

"Sure there are. But they don't come here. Or if they do, they don't stay."

"No one stays for long. There's a lot of die-off."

"Don't exaggerate. Sure, the druggies die young. But there's a lot of guys like him," Rod said. "Gals too." He pointed his chin at one of the local patriarchs, a withered, old white man with an eternal grin showing through his tumbled-gray beard. He was wearing his usual outfit of baggy camo pants under a knee-length rainbow robe. Another lost hippie who thought it was still 1969 and he still meant something. "I swear I saw that guy here when I was a kid, and he looked just as old back then."

"You really believe it's the same guy?"

"I don't believe anything I see here," Rod said. "Even in the mirror. Especially in the mirror."

"How much time do you spend looking into a mirror on the Boardwalk?"

"Every time I buy a pair of sunglasses from Howard the Punk. He's got a mirror on his stand. They always look better there than when I get home. It's some kind of trick mirror, I'm sure of it."

"Howard the Punk isn't together enough to set up a trick mirror. You're just too cheap to buy a good pair at a drugstore. And too lazy not to lose them."

He squinted back at me. He'd already lost this week's pair. "Howard's a good guy," he said.

"Didn't say he wasn't. Just said he wasn't put together too tight. Say it ain't so, if you want, but he's a mess."

Rod shrugged and turned to look at one of the local artists setting up a row of stiffly-painted portraits in shades of pale green. She was wearing what looked like a very short printed dress and no underwear, and she showed some well-toned butt cheeks every time she squatted down to adjust another easel. This was a matter that merited close attention, until I realized that it wasn't a dress she was wearing but a very short jumper with a divided skirt, which rendered the underwear question moot. Still, I kept looking; so did Rod. I'm polite, but I'm still trammeled by male genetics, so of course I looked.

"Guess it works to bring in business," Rod said.

"Assuming any straight guy even looks at the paintings."

"They'll have to pretend to, if only to shut the wife up."

"And they'll still suffer for it. Women aren't as stupid as we are."

"How stupid are we, anyway? You're always saying things like that."

"We're sitting here, aren't we? Eating fried grease and staring at women we'll never meet. Then we'll go back to digging holes in someone else's yard to plant vegetables they'll never remember to harvest. And we're luckier than these clowns. No wonder they're always stoned."

"They're not always stoned," Rod said.

"How many of them do you even know? Besides Howard the Punk?"

"Well, I know Fat Bob. He doesn't get stoned too much."

"The postcards guy?"

"Yeah, him."

"Great. He's the guy the customers have to wake up so he'll sell them a five-dollar postcard. Which is a lot for a postcard."

"He makes them himself. Takes the pictures and everything."

"He sleeps on a boat. At least that's what he told me."

"And do you even have a boat?"

"No. But if I did, I wouldn't have to sleep in it."

"Maybe he just likes the ocean."

"Maybe he's a bum."

"But a sober one," Rod said. "That was my point."

"Okay," I said. "So there's sober bums. What kind of a point is that?" I didn't really want to know, but Rod took it as a challenge.

"Come on," he said. "We've still got half an hour. Let's go visit him. He's usually set up a block away."

Rod got up. I figured I may as well follow him. We went out on the boardwalk and joined the crowd, dodging clusters of sunstruck tourist flesh and being dodged in our turn by the skate punks flitting through the crowd like mangy swallows. We passed by two henna tattoo stands, which were doing pretty good business with the daughters of Midwestern car salesmen and realtors; a stand selling hash pipes; Howard the Punk's sunglass kiosk, where Rod stopped to buy yet another pair of cheap Taiwanese shades; a little clearing where three withered, old white men were playing the blues through a tiny amplifier; and then, just past a squad of fake Gypsy fortunetellers, Fat Bob's postcard stand. A fleshy blonde woman in green hotpants and pink sunburn was closely studying a picture of a muscleman, which Bob had taken twenty years ago a mile up the boardwalk. Her husband waited patiently in the sun, staring past her at a voluptuous six-foot-tall black woman wearing nothing but sandals and a few shreds of macramé and striking poses for tips. Bob stared placidly at the sunburned woman, telling her the story of the muscleman, who had gone on to host a cable TV talk show about life on the beach. The show had gone off the air before the gal was out of high school, most likely, but it was stardom of a sort, and she nodded while Bob droned on. At last she handed him a fiver, and Bob slid the picture into a glassine envelope and sent her on her way. Then he turned to us. "Hey, what brings you here?"

"You do," Rod said. "Just wanted to say Hi."

Bob arranged himself in the beach chair that was the throne of his little empire. As my eyes adjusted better to the shade of the canvas pavilion, I noticed that an old man was sitting in the chair next to him, grubbing at an

74

unidentifiable edible in one of those Styrofoam coffins the eateries used for takeout in those days. I nudged Rod and whispered to him, "Hey, it's the old guy in the rainbow robe!"

Rod nodded. "Yeah, I thought he'd be here. It's Thursday, after all." He spoke in normal tones, so Bob could hear him.

"What's Thursday got to do with it?" I said.

"Hey, Bob, he wants to know what's so special about Thursday."

Bob stirred himself in the creaking chair and smiled, as much as he ever smiled. His expression never varied too far in any one direction. "That's Angel's day to visit." He pointed his chin towards the old man, who was still grubbing food into his beard. "We all take turns buying him lunch. I got him something from the curry stand. Too hot for me, but he likes it." He turned and spoke into the old man's ear: "Tastes good, Angel? They do it the way you like?"

The old man looked up and nodded. Bob turned back to us. "Tomorrow's Zephyr's day. But she only buys him hamburgers. She had a fight with the curry gal. You guys working?"

"About a block away this week," Rod said. "Keeping the rich folks knee-deep in tomatoes and cukes. Like they need a fucking victory garden. I'll bring you some when they're ready."

"Thanks. Want a postcard?"

"Anything new?"

"Got one of Angel. Caught him in the golden hour, take a look."

He handed a card to us. It was the old man, all right. The sunset light streaked across his face as he stood on the beach with his arms spread wide and the wind ruffling his beard. A squad of gulls hovered in the air behind him like dirty cherubs. Everything glowed. The old man looked happy. It was really a pretty good photo.

I looked at the real-life old man hunched in the lawn chair with his face in the Styrofoam carton. Not much of an angel now. But then, what did I know about it; I lived in an apartment in one of those 1970s buildings that are always painted beige, and I didn't even know who lived in the unit next door, except that she was kind of cute. I butted in, "Damn good photo, Bob. The old man looks great. Like a real angel."

"Yeah," Bob grunted. He rummaged in a box and handed me another copy of the photo. "Take it if you want it. Free. I guess it's one of my best."

"Hey, I've got five bucks, I can pay."

"Hey, nothing. We're all friends here." He turned and spoke into the old man's ear again. "Right, Angel? We're all friends here, aren't we?" The old man looked up from his curry and nodded vigorously. "I only charge the tourists," Fat Bob said.

"We're all tourists in this life," Rod said.

"Not on the boardwalk," Fat Bob said. "This is our little bit of heaven." He turned to the old man's ear again. "Right, Angel? The boardwalk is our little heaven on earth, isn't it?"

The old man looked up and smiled. His lips glowed curry-yellow through his beard, and his smile shone like the sunrise.

Rod looked at me and winked. I winked back, but I really didn't mean it. I'm not sure what I meant.

On the way home, I bought a frame for the picture of Angel on the beach. It really was a pretty good picture. And Fat Bob hadn't been stoned. Rod was right for a change. Anything can happen on the boardwalk. Anything at all.

Amorphogermen titanum

Lee Landey

Today I returned to the garden. Coming north, the train ducks underground a few stops before spitting out over the western burgs. I've lost my job, so it's around eleven I get moving, the sun diagonal on the haze and sparking the hump of the botanicum as we rattle around the old depots and into view. Eleven is the slow hour, when everyone should be where they're going. A wheezing snore next to me dips with the car's rocking. She probably spent the night on the train. A ratty jacket covers her head. Eleven. I used to sort mail downtown. There's less mail now, but who knows what that says. Do people talk less? I do. But in the street it's like everyone is talking. There's no corner of silence in Franklin. Every tunnel has its drips and moans, and the garden its green hiss and library mutters. The empty train screams.

My mother's mother came to Franklin City sixty years ago from out east. She ran the wrong way, but lots made that mistake. The garden wasn't new then either. From some war before that one. She's who told me about the flower. She said it was there before they built the garden. I don't know how that could be true, but she said so.

My grandmother liked plants. She knew things. She came from far outskirts, where they only caught a ration from bigger places of sound and chaos, in their kitchen, den, the woods behind their house. She talked about the early times in Franklin, before my mother was born, when she would come to the garden and sit by herself under the big glass dome and listen to the jungle rush, waiting for the Dead Flower to bloom; *Amorphogermen titanum*. That's the Latin. It bloomed erratically, a purple hand flopping open to spill rotten honey on its neighbors, once, twice every hundred years. The color of eggplant twilight, springing wide to drown near flowers and waxy ferns in syrup and then hibernate for another generation. Why'd they let it be, if it wanted so much for itself? The spectacle, for one. Franklin likes a strong competitor, she said. Franklin likes a rarity.

She spoke of a petal at the center. The Dead Petal, if we're keeping with idiot names. A different shade of violet, with a red eyelet, and a point like a knife. My young grandmother, sitting patiently in nude tights with her handbag, waited for the lusty time when the flower would pop. She wanted the petal. And why? She never said. But all those years later in the run-down home on Bleecker Street after Mom died, still it stuck its knifepoint through her brain fog enough that even then, to me, she thought to mention it.

The flower shows signs, she said, before it pops. When she first came to Franklin it was budding, prodding from the wet earth with unripe elbow.

That means come back soon and keep watch. So she had come. She worked days then as a typesetter for the *Herald*, living on her own in a small Southtown flat. Each day after work she'd put in the time, till evening and the botanicum's closing gates, and all weekends with the weak sun on the windows. For if she was there when it popped, she had a chance.

When the time's near, she said, it rises like a bent snake, its shriveled neck dragging the ground. The unfolding is quick, its nauseous odor renowned. Then the splash of sweet bitters, the encircling flora withers, and the red-eyed petal smiles up piston-hard.

Be watchful or you'll miss it.

She missed it.

The day it blossomed was the day of the Big Quake, and is thus overshadowed in record and memory. She rode the F train that Saturday morning toward the botanicum when the rail over Westriver shattered, and its passengers found themselves gripping white-knuckled to plastic seatbacks as they dangled over the steep embankment and sludgy trough below. It did, in fact, collapse, sending two dozen on a bumpy ride through rancid rapids, resulting in half as many deaths. My unwed grandmother clung desperately to a dislodged luggage rack beside a young man she would come to spend a number of unhappy years with, until his own demise in duller days from a lung condition. They managed to conceive my mother between these episodes.

And what about the flower? By the time she made it back to the garden, after a brief stint at St. Rags Memorial with a bruised temple and jangled nerves, it was curled sleeping amid its desolation, a wrinkled brown thing in the dirt. Spoiled circlets of ferns swept in low waves from the epicenter. It was a poison pebble on the earthen pond.

She died in the home on Bleecker Street, alone but for the overworked help. I'd see her sometimes, a weekend now and then. I'd bring flowers. I think I missed the point. She told me so, anyway. It wasn't until layoffs that I thought about it, years after she was gone. One misty morning, waking to find a dry vine crawling over the small window of my apartment, I reeled in bed to the purple silhouette, as she'd described, dressing the back of my eyelids.

It's coming, is what I've learned. These days the pale green elbow juts amid bracken, sucking the last moisture from old kills. The mail's dried up so I watch from the clamorous woods, alive with mister-hiss and visitors. The interregnum is ending. The pogrom will come soon.

By the time I reach the garden it's nearly noon, and the glass plates of the dome radiate heat under a low haze. I take the southern entrance, strolling past the visitor center and its rheumy minder toward branching footpaths. This way passes first through the deserts, with pale sands and ribbed cactus. Taller specimens are crowned in clusters of pink florets, and a species of hummingbird has been allowed to propagate for purposes of pollination. Their hurried wingbeats trace low altitudes, pushing feather-breath currents as I navigate a grove of thorns. I find an arid introduction eases my transition to the jungle dark.

Past the desert comes dusty outback, with peeling eucalyptus and flat acacia vying for space. Some kids jaunt through the pathless dirt. Beyond lies the palm garden, where small ponds collect sagging fronds in an obstacle course for turtles. Sometimes I'll stop here, where it's most quiet. Today I push ahead, first to lilies, and past the white library. A bridge crosses the water. Next come roses, a crazed arrangement of color, under-pruned and wild, clawing over the path with brittle spines. And finally, behind fogged glass, dripping hot with condensation, the heavy green looms.

I shoulder through the suction seal of doors as the customary damp slaps my cheeks and jacket. A lungful of water and I'm slouching ahead past dim couples in the mist. The Dead Flower waits left of center, crouched below a long girder of dome. My shirt's plastered to me by the time I reach our favored bench, a low iron thing beside the plot's enclosure. Now, mostly, I sit.

These days the garden is in disrepair, somehow under-watered but overgrown. The desert hummingbirds have run wild, and elsewhere brown vines overtake unswept paths. City money wanders to other ventures while the garden festers, a forgotten project. Still, admission is free. One walks into a forested bus stop. If you were to wander gloomy paths you might find errant couples humping against trees in the mist, or groaning junkies under wet ferns. I sit where my grandmother sat in more subsidized days, and stare at the stubborn green nub where it pokes from the earth. On a hot day like today, faintly the expanding girders can be heard to creak high above in the foggy roof. The environment controls gutter with white noise, and two young men recline against the banister smoking wet cigarettes. The jungle has its regulars.

These two I catch on occasion, slipping through the fog. Brothers or friends, I can't be sure, always they bring a wind of sodden tobacco, each with a small shape tattooed below his eye. Often I find them crouched in the mangroves, playing cards. Others I know by shapes and colors, distorted through distance and foliage. There's sweeps now and then to keep out vagrants, but endless crannies and dells for hiding. A network of homeless thrive in deeper woods and under bridges. Don't drink, say the lakeside signs. Anyhow, I like it.

I sit today in wetness, and ponder what I'll do when it hatches. How I'll clamber over the iron railing and wade through ferns, pluck the Dead Petal and disappear into fog. And what'll I do with the petal? Plant it? Maybe it'll grow me a job. I've worn galoshes for the purpose, to guard against the nectar. Who knows its strength? My grandmother knew, but never said. I've checked the white library, pored over logs of this place's other growths. For my quarry, the entry says this:

Amorphogermen titanum; Dead Flower. Rare.

I've visited the *Herald's* records, scrolling till purblind through tarry microfiche. Local interest? Where does one look for these things? There's mention of a happening at the garden 132 years ago. A news item and its subheading from that day read:

Spectacular Spectacle at Franklin Botanicum!
Good Folks from our Good City gather at World's Finest for a glimpse of Something New

It proceeds:

Franklin's resident green thumbs will be delighted to hear what's happening at the storied gallery of worldly (and otherworldly!) plants. For nature lovers everywhere, a rare treat buds on the horizon! (cont'd page 4)

Page 4, and the rest of that week's papers, are of course missing. One thing I have learned in the sorting of envelopes is that there are no answers to anything.

There exists another brief account from the time of my grandmother's tenure at the *Herald*. Whether she had a hand in its mention I can't say. Buried four columns into a front-page story relating the various damages of the Big Quake, there appears the line:

Fearful for the remaining sections of elevated rail, city officials evacuated all stations north of Westriver, while nearby Frankliners fled the scene of a purportedly chaotic bloom at the Municipal Botanicum.

How devastating a bloom? How deep run its roots? Lounging in wetness with the green perfume of rot, I think back to those wan days in the home on Bleecker Street. What did she tell me? The stupid fact is that I never listened. I visited from guilt or some poorer motive. She sat in the dingy bed and looked at my flowers, mouthing, "Matthew, Matthew, I'm sore, my knees are through, and the help is nicking my silver." It's easy to look at that pathetic thing and think only, *I wish my obligation were ended.*

I would sit in a folding chair in the corner while she whined. She'd relax when tea came and talk about plants, the trees behind her childhood home, the sidewalk weeds in Southtown. My eyes remained half-closed. It was only with the dream, when the dry vine crawled over my small window, and she was years dead. A vision of purple in the worm-filled earth, while in the morning I filled out personal statistics for a food security program. Only from a dream did I make the trek to Franklin's dilapidated garden, with phantoms of my grandmother wafting through jungle shade. To prowl the iron-ringed paths in search of a seedbed, slouch on low benches and wonder what she had said about the flower. It was high fancy, I remember that much. A sexless thing, or two-sexed? Anyway, it didn't breed, only slept and grew. It was the finale of carnivores.

When my grandmother died, I got rid of her effects. Mom was already gone and couldn't protest. What was I supposed to do with all of it? My apartment barely fits me and a bed. So there were old journals of hers, books and bottles, pillowcases of letters and ephemera that went out the back door of the home and on to the confetti piles of the Franklin dump, out west beyond the last factory.

Hovering in the fog, up where the sun makes limp attempts at the glass, mingling with her musty presence are visions of scrawled pages, all the notes and decades of theory in her neat hand. If she was still talking about the flower in twilight years while I sat like a limp fish in the corner, how much had she written of it in those piles of notebooks? What secrets and marvels, biological facts had she recorded, and anyway, how did she know? And why can I only care once something's gone?

The two men smoking cigarettes wander off to shadow. A pitcher plant entices a snail to explore its innards. The Dead Flower looks placid for now, so I make off down dappled paths. Two figures slump at the roots of a rubber tree, asleep or near enough. Pushing past waxy fronds, I discover a shopping cart dragged to its ribs by ivy.

Some days I dream I could be the postman for this place. Surely the makeshift community would write. I could sort their letters in the deserts, walk the paths to every vine-hammock and under-bridge where they hide. I could bear it all.

I take a detour through mangroves to find the men at their cards, and duck off the path to wade. There are flowers, secret growths that perk up white from the bog. I like to look, now and again, and think I'm the only one who knows of them. I think of how I would relate them to my grandmother; what facts are of chief importance. The stalks are thin, and the faces hang with pale legs like dancers. They grow in water, so there's that. What else could I say?

I climb over roots at the far side of the bog, and back onto the encircling path. Two women give a wide berth as I lumber from the foliage, my sodden shoes leaking brown water. When I return to the Dead Flower, it has another visitor.

Dappled brown skin, with rough curls pulled back behind her nape and sprouts of gray starting to show. A dirt-colored cardigan over black skirts. She leans on the banister, craning her neck above the unripe nub with strands of hair falling about her face, lips moving. I can't hear what she says over the white hiss of mist. The fog blares.

I sit on the bench and let her speak. A palm lazes high above. I fall asleep. When I come to she's beside me, filing her nails. Small moles cluster around her eyes. A lost hummingbird jogs by.

"Long night?" she asks.

"Not really."

"I recognize you."

"Yeah," I nod. "You talk to it?"

"You don't?" A hunched figure tows a shopping cart past our bench.

"I haven't tried that, no."

"What do you know about it?" she asks.

"What do *you* know about it?"

She stares me down. Above the moles, pale dots crowd on the whites of her eyes.

"I know I'm waiting," she offers.

"Yeah."

"How do you know about it?" she asks.

"It's no big secret."

"I don't see anyone else here."

"A relative," I shrug. "A relative told me. She was really interested."

"And now you are too?"

"Sure," I squint. "How do you know about it?"

"My great uncle." She purses her lips. "They used to write about it in the paper, you know. Oh, they don't write about anything anymore. But they did. He was here the last time."

"When the Quake…?"

"When the Quake," she nods.

"Did he see it?"

She pulls out a slim cigarette.

"He saw it."

"What did he see?"

A low flame struggles through sheets of mist. She takes a drag, and smoke curls from her nose to mix with steam.

"He was after that petal."

"Why?" I stutter.

"'Why?'" she mimics. "Same as anyone. He said when it happened there was a wave of burning, and everybody ran. He says the Quake came only after the bloom."

"You mean to say…?"

"Mm," she nods. "I mean to say. Roots down to the bedrock."

"I'm Matthew." I reach out my hand. She takes it with square nails.

"Hello Matthew. I'm Matilda."

"I've seen you," I say lamely.

"My great uncle," she smokes, "would give me potted plants when I was a little girl. He worked at a nursery. That was how I knew him. He could never afford to retire. He had a hard time talking. It wasn't his first language. But I could never talk to my mother either. The air in Franklin is terrible for gardening, but we had a small trough on the balcony where he helped me plant fruits and vegetables. Tomatoes and carrots mostly. We never managed a crop, they'd wither on the vine and the carrots would come up shriveled, but he showed me with your hands how to push the dirt, and the stakes for support. That was how we communicated. He took me here, to the garden, a few times when I was young. Anyhow, he got the story across. We'd use this bench, and he showed me with his hands how a girder fell, and all of it. He died a long time ago. But I remember."

"Why would they let it live? The flower?"

"Maybe Franklin needs a little death," she shrugs.

"I can't find anything about it, you know. I've been around. The library here, the records at the paper. People know it, in a way; 'Oh yeah,' they say, 'the flower,' but no one can tell you anything. Nothing that gets across. Like they went through everybody and removed the communicable facts."

"'They?'" she mimics.

"Whoever," I shrug. "And the petal?"

"I don't know, Matthew. I only know what he told me."

* * *

I head home before it gets dark. The train is still empty, the sleeping woman still asleep. I make the endless climb to my apartment and slump through the door, unreasonably tired. These days the dry vines all but cover my window, pinpricks of city peeping through. The jungle fog has followed me home, and I sink into bed with leaden limbs.

In a dream my grandmother is a tree. Great branches spread to a white sky, and fat fruit hangs from her. Knobby green things with rough skin, I twist one from its branch and settle between two sloping roots. A white wind stirs the grass, and toward the horizon something grows. I gash the fruit with a thumbnail and work at the peel, looking up through twisting leaves at the flat sky. Mindlessly I strip away the pith. When I look to my hands, the fleshy fruit is the face of my mother. My thumb uncovers her hair.

* * *

Over gray weeks I return to the garden. I still have my apartment for now, but sometimes I'll sleep the night there by the mangroves, or pondside below a bridge. With my ear to the dirt I imagine that I can hear the throbbing roots readying, where they reach to lightless depths and tectonic caves. Maybe in those pits I could sort the mail, and distribute the world's words through woody capillaries and fungal partners. Somewhere must be the place.

Matilda often shares our bench, dressed in drabs and smoking thin cigarettes. We don't talk much. We both feel it coming. The city has forgotten, its papers blank, but the two of us wait while the green elbow turns from the earth with a sickle frown. We fall asleep together some days, watching. We eat little, but I'll share with her a sandwich if I've thought to bring it. Watercress is my favorite. She likes the cucumber.

Afternoons pass and I'm broke. I wait in brown fog for help from the city. I look for listings in the paper. I'm a mail sorter, I tell them. I fall asleep in the desert. As though the moon descends from space, a shadow lengthens. Streets are stretched, ready to blister. Everywhere is chatter, the trains, bus depots, kiosks or shoreside. A swelling murmur that makes less sense the louder it grows.

We wake together on the bench one afternoon to find the elbow has come unstuck, and now drags a withered neck through the dirt. Neighboring ferns bend away in distress. There is a stirring over my gut, nauseous, while Matilda's old hand grips my arm. Above, the glass and girders creak with consternation. Two vagrants run past, accompanied by hummingbirds. The jungle doors thrust open, and a rattle of voices travels in from the rose garden. The purple head splits.

I am struck blind as the commotion hits, and the flower rises for me in darkness with acid fountains, and night frogs hiccoughing in the abyss. I bound forward dumbly. The jungle shakes, and I am alone in a world of dragging vines and green heaven. Like the roots have thrust up as legs, and the whole botanicum has wandered crashing into downtown, all the frighted clerks, homeless, middle managers fleeing in a clash of glass and plant matter. Like Matilda and I stand at the rocking helm of this great craft ready for the stars, one spider-leg root-leap away from new worlds. Like we are the galloping word-life of all animals. I am startled from dreams by the screaming odor of dissolving ferns.

Matilda reaches for the railing as the ground trembles under a tide of hot nectar. The soles of her flats sizzle, and she cries out. I run ahead in my galoshes as she pounces, yowling, onto my back. Brilliance streams through girders. The great purple fist unfurls in golden light.

The petal rises. Matilda reaches a trembling hand. My eyes stream, swollen. Junkies flee over quaking paths while our little plot explodes. For a moment I think the dome will collapse around our ears in brittle dust. Then it is done; the vision fades. The ground settles. The Dead Flower curls, lilting toward us in a bow. The petal brushes my face. A wind feathers the trees. Matilda has it.

The garden is silent. A hairline crack runs through the concrete below our bench. The garden is intact. Dead plants lie around, oozing. The bloom is over. A hummingbird rides past.

Matilda holds out the petal to me, a maroon thing, throbbing faintly. Its little eye peeps up at the haze. She keeps it balanced on her palm as I brush it with a forefinger. It burps, and something viscous seeps onto her wrist.

"Does it burn?" I whisper.

"A little."

***

I let Matilda into my apartment. She huffs. Bad knees, she explains. She looks around at the bed, walls, window, where dry vines show a hint now of green and other colors.

"Well," she says. She pulls a chair up and sits.

"No so bad as the last one," I remark, standing. "The city survived, at least."

She nods. "I bet you it's the next one. The next one will be big." She places the petal on the table where it flops like a child, kaput after long afternoons.

"What do we do with it?" I wonder. She smooths it out, letting it drip on the wood.

"I have an idea."

I rest while Matilda putters around my kitchen. I can barely stand. Mutters beat at the window and its flowering vines. A train rips past on high rails beside the old park. From what sky I can see, something writhes under cloud cover. I close my eyes. And what of postage?

Matilda approaches me on the bed, pepper hair falling over her shoulders. She holds two steaming mugs.

"Here," she offers, settling beside me. I struggle to sit. "I boiled it down. The petal." I take a sniff. "You like tea?" she asks.

"Sure."

It's bittersweet, like a pulp of cranberries, anise, and something gone off. It burns a little. Mostly it tastes of hot water. I get it down. Matilda finishes and wipes her mouth with a brown sleeve.

"How do you feel?" she asks, holding her head.

"Awake," I shrug.

I shift to make room, and she pulls her knees up, placing her small bulk on the mattress beside me.

"I had a husband, you know," she says.

"Yeah?"

"He moved to a different city."

"Where would you go?"

"There's places," she affirms. "They don't put that in the paper anymore. But there's all kinds of places. Out west past the fog. He took a road car; it was mine too, is how I know."

"Why did he go?"

"We never were in the same place anymore. Not really. He lost my dictionary, is what he said. But there's all kinds of places."

"I never really met anybody," I shrug.

"Well," she stretches her small arms toward the ceiling and makes a noise in her throat. "There's time."

All that night we stay up, and talk and talk and talk.

***

In a dream I am in my bed, and Matilda is beside me. The sun is down, and the vines at the window have come alive in the night. Colorful thorns and buds snicker and ribbit, trembling at the panes. I try to move, but find I am fused to the bed. A growth of fibers has crept from my skin and woven into the blanket; woven into Matilda. The flesh of her arm touches me. Fibers from us puddle together, and coil in heat. The fragile skin of her wrist slops against mine, while vines thrash at the window. Her eyes are closed; her sleeping head seeps against my chest. Her jowl conjoins to my nipple. She sighs a sleepy sigh. I feel it in my lungs. Above us, in the dark, stands my grandmother. But my grandmother is no longer a tree. She is just a person.

* * *

We sit up. Morning light seeps whitely through the window. We stand. We stretch. Yawn, yowl. We slip on our flats. Flats don't fit. We walk to the washroom, look in the mirror. We muss our hair. We brush our teeth. Toothpaste tastes bad. We put a shirt on. Shirt doesn't fit. We grab our biggest jacket and toss it around our shoulders. We leave our small apartment. We go nimbly down the stairs.

In hazy morning we pad the pavement. The brown smudge has moved east, and light is coming through. We hum deeply as we walk and bump into lots of little people. All the people look at us. We say hello to them all. We know where we are going. It is a beautiful morning for walking, as these things go.

We stride lightly to the post office. We pull open the glass doors and duck under the lintel past our purple reflection. Very low, and the ceilings too. The people in the post office look at us. Some even point. We walk to the small stations with pens and paper for writing, envelopes for sending. The people make room for us. They step aside and stare up with wide eyes. We have much to say, so we take a pen and paper to set down some thoughts. We address an envelope to the Franklin dump.

"Dear Mothers," we begin.

ONE POEM

Ivana Mestrovic

A Short Story About Love

I gave the man a hat.
It had been worn before.

"Please put it on,"
I said. He did

for he was kind.
He wore it for awhile

gladly as if it fit him,
as if it were his own.

Indeed the band conformed
to him with wearing

and our weather.
In the end we parted

and divvied up our lots.
I am back where once I started.

The hat is mine again
but not.

TWO POEMS

David M. Alper

Soft Lividness Is Wintry

A brisk breeze is on
the horizon
a great willow long ago
burned
down to its roots.
Crops are still buried
under
a great hill.
The clouds have tumbled
against one another
lashing
at the dead of night
with dreadful lightening
into the dark;
I still have not figured out
how to go with one foot in front of the other
as I go
through this life.

But now I can walk
in fresh air
with arms
bound together
for the night
in a sturdy embrace.
In a warm room
as evening descends
silence cloaks the yard
crickets are heard
clicking like billiard balls.
When I walk
behind my favorite tree
the breezes whisper
the trees breathe
a sigh of undying love
for each other
and the sky.

The Calcinations Blue the Hurricane

a flashlight in the nacelle with its wick the light of your world
the fingers of mine that hold yours at sea's sigh
and again the starlight
the moonlight
the ocean lapping
against the side of your house
we are tangled like the rays of a caress
like the strands of a rope
that are meant to be braided
and unbraided
as they rise
and fall
like the earth in the sunrise
like a waterspout
from a hurricane
that swirls in
like a dream
the receding tide's final touch
and then the shore is sandy
and long
in my arms
the blue
lifted from the sea
drift back to the sky
and the words that were so aptly
descriptive of a path of romance.

FOUR POEMS

RC de Winter

ancient wisdom

there was a
time when i cut those
who wronged me
off with no
remorse but i've learned that was
the wrong thing to do

because those
who are out to get
you never
give up and
there you are ignorant of
the slings and arrows

still volleyed
your way damaging
you in the
eyes of the
world so now i keep a line
open to the word on

the street and
though i refuse to
interact
i know their treachery
and can deflect the

ugliness
of others without
directly
addressing
it — Sun Tzu said *keep friends close*
enemies closer

scuppered

it's been an impossible day
full of nothing but frustration and regret
so i opened my tattered bag of coins
and tried to bribe the universe
but the only answer
was the laughter of invisible gods

sorrow flowed over the dam of my heart
decorating it with hairline cracks
guaranteeing a continual trickle
just enough to stain every day
no matter how happy with a tinge of blue
a constant reminder of all my losses

there's no arguing with heartache
it's deaf to all but what it carries
the slow steady stream of what could have —
should have — been the unresurrectable joy
of life in the key of love now muted
by the laughter of those indifferent gods

waiting for the wind

lately i'm often lost for hours
musing on what was and what might or might not be
in places having nothing to do with the here and now
the present is no present to me
an autumn leaf loosed from the mother tree
fallen gently into wonderland
with no firm fix but the moist hungry earth
on which i rest
hoping for the rescue of a gentle wind
to take me somewhere beautiful
uncluttered with the past

sunday coffee god and all the rest of it

i sit sipping coffee by the window in the kitchen
as the procession of the faithful summoned by sunday bells begins
car after car carrying people dressed up for god and each other
rolling by on the way to whatever form of worship soothes their souls

but i an impenitent unbeliever reject the credulity called faith
that's been fractured and reshaped into innumerable incarnations
and whether or not there's a judgmental old man in the sky
remain unworried about my final disposition

i haven't been good enough to deserve heaven
nor bad enough to deserve hell
so if he exists i'll be lounging in some nebulous corner of the universe
with the vast majority of the great unwashed
where the law of averages reigns
which is pretty much an approximation of the way i'm living now

TWO POEMS

Gale Acuff

One day I'm going to die and I don't

want to but that doesn't matter, it will
happen and I'll be right there with it and
it's natural they say at regular
school but at church and Sunday School even
though it's also natural it's to be
avoided but only by preparing
for it, saving all you can of yourself
— that would be your soul, as for your body
it's kind of a lost cause but always was
and probably always knew it would be
crucified so what's left is Heaven and
Hell, at our church at least, and the better
choice is Heaven, which is good, I think,
but I'll miss my body. We're pretty close.

My sister's building something with sugar

cubes and when she turns her back I sneak a
sweet brick but I don't know it's got the mor
-tar of Elmer's glue on it so I get
sick and retch like a son of a bitch and
I guess I was lucky that I didn't
choke to death or unlucky that she did
-n't, which is terrible of me to say
but then I'm thinking for me then, not now,
and as for the future she died last week
and there are half a house's worth of bricks
or blocks or just plain unglued cubes
left and I'd build her a mausoleum
in miniature but I bet I'd eat
it before it was done. That's kind of sweet.

THREE POEMS

Massimo Fantuzzi

[Duality no.3]

To riven,

Neither flows nor sloughs,

Oblivious the sickle to its own fury,

Stinger, to its honeyed kiss.

Quasi senz'onda,

Feverish skin of ashen texture
      (medicinal itching gone for the trenches)
Drowsy, his drained face
      (callous soil, eyelids, crying slabs)
Elongated intentions shadowbox ahead in the red evening's carmine.

Will this last strike of cobalt ever sprout?
      (burial, echo, sprout, sprout)
Spatchcocked between opposite piano keys?
      (him and his Finale, these unlit candelabras)

Medusa, rossa medusa.

Blood on shirt and grey cufflinks choked in bugs and worms the far side of this oak torso spirit of the thousands march above him like a spotlight over one next town in pompous dissertation over parting rituals the Road is woman pastel brightens the sand rinsed by sweat spill and fatigue I reappear.

Spring Rite

(Milonga in Sirmione, 1991)

(Enter Water)
Sight of you, longed spectacle poured and parched
over the end of lines. Contemplative blackness
breathe in concert on this lake on this oily night.

Through our toes runs our dare, rock and water
disappearing traded with the prickly frosts of a million burns,
each tide of a blush and a promise. *Count my curls,*
each ripple throb fostering our pull.

(Enter Earth)
Fleeted under a crammed moon *und* woodland,
young bodies gesture forth. Twos in twos, carved in full
sur la paumé of promenades, foreign beauties, odors and similes.

My brittle friend the iron taste queues up nostrils and palate
where sibyls' corpses are still crawling sifted: some dried copper,
some bronzed jar looms of a humble swelled mound,
and posthumously over our neatly soften forms and caked nails.

(Enter Fire)
Gradually carved, little gush: Verb miracle of savannah,
those two lapilli your newest blood irks and sears
the surface the branded skin forever sculpted.

Blossom, blisters ring to life
blinds in scratches and cherry sweat
lines and palms open to protect, complicit with every thrust,
having just about remembered where the key is.

(Enter Wind)
Hum and spin, what ravenous walls
the jingle jangle of chrysanthemum
around your back tattooed might instill.

To make whole of spheres again, hunted tongues
lap within me silvered sprayed and charred slung. All their trembled pry
is to replay thy coy run in the shower, thy even shyer return,
and how we've left Mamma Giliola with the mop-up of her lifetime.

(All leave)

Here and There, a Glimpse through the Abbey
(The importance of review and metacognition)

Scribble of this holding hands during showers of resonance, swerving nude
meadow longing armistice to where the grain is fair,
to the other side where martyr of bitterly perfumed parsley
mash into a most disharmonious bridleway of lop-sided penance.

B: *(Staring at the man unconscious on the bed center stage. Long pause.)*
Sure you are not mistaken?

A: Have I ever been mistaken?

B: Mistaken. Once. Give it here. *(Grabs a stack of loose pages from T. Quickly glances through then points out a particular paragraph on one of the sheets.)* There! Velvet. Took it for violet and sold it back to him. That finished him.

Winter's growing will cover for small appearances
staring at the glass where sincere necessities
will pace a fantasy embracing snap of treasured manners, a gone
parade of modest bread conversed of oil and aniseed for good luck.

A: Call that a mistake!

B: Botched rationale.

I pray. Your skin to materialize again brighter, tailored ordeal
conned to dress more and remember less, here to tell
the ensured and the encompassed where to joy and not to nest.

A: The outcomes! See? The end product. *(Points somewhere above their heads.)* Sitting on the top branch. Third from the left. Quarter down. Plummy and titillating: simple question of fruition!

B: *(Opens his arms.)* These the sweetest fruits we've had in years. And the sweetest they are, look. *(Points at the man occupying the bed.)* The messiest they land.

A: You shouldn't make fun of him: without him…

B: *(Exasperated, slaps the papers with the back of his hand.)* They have never really met! Did you forget that?

A: *(Snatches the paper from B. Quickly glances through.)* A little dancing went on. *(Points out a particular paragraph on one of the sheets.)* Here! We have the vomit incident outside her car, 3 Russel Square, pass the steps, pass the aqueduct. There is the episode of the frozen dinner, Chez-Luca of 47 Jordan Avenue. *(Pause.)* In addition to that… *(Browses further.)* Here! At least three locations, three, visited, spent, engraved, recorded all in accordance with the best-of-the-century practice.

B: Derails, seaward, noting more, off they went and by looking at him, might be the reason why streets around here still spell inhabitable.

A: Something will grow back, it always does.

You to stay. Part to canvas, to cast aligned new skies.
At your tortured feet: I am your useless dying sister to bless
to verge grass or country lane, to drain
lead and pore a cover over the balcony of my motives undone.

Dark Matter

Mark Scharf

> "The past is what you remember, imagine you remember, convince yourself you remember, or pretend you remember."
>
> –Pinter

Characters

A: 50's/60's, any race and gender
B: 50's/60's, any race and gender
C: 50's/60's, any race and gender

Setting

The Present. A front room with a window looking out on a front yard.

Scene

(Darkness, then soft dim light that leaves all in silhouette.
As if a switch were flicked "on," an inordinately loud white noise blasts the theater. It holds for a moment then is abruptly switched off.
Silence.
Lights rise revealing A is standing while B sits. B holds and presses a few buttons, then holds it out towards A.)

(A's VOICE from the Cell Phone Speaker:)
Hi... Guess you're busy. Listen... please give me a call as soon as you can. Something's wrong. I came downstairs and I don't know what I'm doing. Something is wrong. I'm very confused. I'm looking out the window and I don't know what I'm doing. I don't know what's going on. I'm confused. I'm very... confused. Call me back. Okay. Bye.
A: I don't remember saying that.
B: None of it?
A: I remember making the call — that I called you.
B: Want to hear it again?
A: It won't help.

B: But you remember making the call...
A: Yes, I remember that much.
B: I called you back when I got the message. You kept saying it was Monday and you had a lot of work to do. But it was Wednesday.
A: I remember being in a conference call earlier — and texting you it was a boring meeting from hell.
B: What was the meeting about?
A: I don't remember what was discussed.
B: Who else was on the call?
A: I don't know exactly.
B: Exactly? So, you remember something.
A: No, but it was a conference call we have once a week. I'm sure the usual suspects were there.
B: But you're guessing?
A: That's right, I can't say for sure. I couldn't swear to anything in a court of law.
B: You must remember something.
A: Why must I remember anything?
B: It made an impression. Something happened — or didn't happen that affected you. You decided it was a boring meeting from hell. You made a judgment based on something.
A: Maybe it just was. Maybe it was an observation. Like the sky is blue or its cold out or that tree is dead.
B: The tree in the front yard?
A: Sure. Why not? The tree in the front yard.
B: Are you sure it's dead?'
A: Very sure. I've looked it at closely. No leaves, stripped of any bark — if it had bark, I don't know. Like an old woman's crooked, skinny finger extended up from the earth pointing at the sky — accusing the heavens of neglect.
B: I see. What kind of tree is it? Or, rather, was it?
A: Who cares what kind of tree it is? It doesn't make any difference; it's dead.
B: So, you say.
A: So, it is.
B: I think it's a Japanese Maple.
A: A dead Japanese Maple.
B: Lots of dead Japanese Maple trees around here. It must be a fungus attacking them.
A: How many?
B: How many what?
A: Dead Japanese Maple trees!
B: I couldn't say. I didn't count them.
A: But you noticed what they were and that they're dead.
B: I suppose so.
A: You suppose? You either did or you didn't.
B: All right, I noticed they were dead Japanese Maple trees.
A: So, we agree on that. We both remember the dead tree.
B: What's next? What's the next thing you recall?

    (Silence.)
A: You coming in through the door. And other people, I think...
B: The ambulance crew.
A: I remember stepping up into the ambulance through its back door — and someone asked me what month it is. I don't remember anything else till I was in the room at the ER. I don't remember the ride or arriving at the hospital or checking in or changing into the gown or speaking with anyone. Not till you were in the room. I don't know how you got there, but I remember you sitting in that white, cramped room.
B: I drove myself. Do you remember them taking blood?
A: No.
B: They took blood for tests. Then they took you for a CAT scan.
A: Don't remember it.
B: You rode in a wheelchair.
A: Damn.
B: What?
A: Damn it!
B: What's the matter?
A: I don't remember riding in an ambulance and I don't remember a wheelchair!
B: Don't get frustrated. It'll make things worse.
A: It can't be worse. I don't remember!
B: Nothing?
A: Flashes — like snapshots really... But these... these moments are islands surrounded by nothing. That's what scares me.
B: Can you describe these snapshots?
A: Images mostly — sometimes snatches of words — like a question.
B: Tell me about the first one — at the beginning of the... the episode.
A: Episode. Sounds like part of a series. "Tune in next week for another exciting episode." Or maybe binge-watch the whole thing at once.
B: Hope not.
A: I don't recall what precipitated my calling you. What happened to make me — that caused me to call you.
B: But you do remember calling...
A: I remember standing here looking out the front window at the yard and the street. Then calling you on my cell — leaving a message because, of course, you didn't answer.
    (Silence.)
A: *(Cont.)* I don't remember everything I said. But that's normal for me... I want to... I need to know what happened.
B: Want to hear your voice mail again?
A: I don't know.
B: Does it scare you?
A: Yes. Yes, it does.
B: It's your voice — your words...
A: That I don't remember saying.
B: It's up to you.

A: Let's hear it then.
B: Sure?
A: Yeah.
B: All right, then.
A: You think?

(B presses a few buttons on the cell phone, then holds it out towards A.)
(A's VOICE from the Cell Phone Speaker:)

Hi… Guess you're busy. Listen… please give me a call as soon as you can. Something's wrong. I came downstairs and I don't know what I'm doing. Something is wrong. I'm very confused. I'm looking out the window and I don't know what I'm doing. I don't know what's going on. I'm confused. I'm very… confused. Call me back. Okay. Bye.

(The white noise assaults the theater again. Only A reacts to it. The noise is switched off.)

B: What's the matter?
A: What?
B: You look scared.
A: Do I?
B: Confused.
A: Because I am. I'm confused about what happened. Frustrated. Worried. Scared that I can't make myself remember. All I have are these impressions…
B: A nurse came in and asked you questions…
A: She had that shiny, silver stethoscope draped around her neck like a mink stole.
B: You couldn't remember its name.
A: I knew what it was for — that you listen to a heart with it. Then she asked me who was the president. I couldn't believe she'd ask me that.
B: Liked your response
A: You mean "that… that bastard?"
B: So, we know your memory isn't totally gone.
A: They stuck that IV needle into my arm. I hate needles. Felt like a railroad spike stuck in my arm.
B: You were extremely dehydrated. They also put a steroid in your IV solution. Something good for your brain. Must've worked cause you whole demeanor changed in less than twenty minutes. I could see you coming back.
A: From where?
B: Somewhere inside that head of yours.
A: I was afraid it was a stroke.
B: So was I. That's why I called for an ambulance. You didn't want me to call. Argued with me about it.
A: You know what that's going to cost?
B: Doesn't matter. They know what to do if it's a stroke. We were in the middle of "the golden hour."
A: I'm worried about money adding up and you're worried about the clock ticking down.
B: It was. If it was a stroke you've got about an hour to deal with it to keep you from dying and to keep any real damage from setting in.

A: I don't remember. Something ate those hours. Erased them completely.
B: Or they never made an impression. Like when you're sleeping. You don't remember what happens to you when you're asleep.
A: I remember my dreams lately.
B: What are they about?
A: They worry me.
B: Of course they do. They're your dreams. Answer the question.
    (Silence.)
A: Mortality.
B: There's a dead end.
A: Not funny.
B: But true. The end.
A: The last word
B: Forget about it.
A: Omnipresent.
B: If you let it be.
A: Avoidance doesn't work
B: Let it be.
A: Must be addressed.
B: Inevitable someday.
A: Maybe today. Could be any day.
B: Only happens once.
A: Which could be today.
B: Nothing you can do.
A: Can't stop thinking...
B: Get a grip.
A: That's cold.
B: Deal with it
A: Insulting.
B: Elephant in the room.
A: And other clichés.
B: Can't outrun it
A: Or ignore it.
B: Set it aside.
A: How?
B: Force of will.
A: Triumph of the will!
B: Strength matters.
A: You despise weakness above all else.
B: Not useful. Not attractive.
A: Nazi.
B: Insult of the last resort.
A: Riefenstahl pin up.
B: You could bounce a quarter off her...
A: Excuses!
B: Facts.

A: As long as you believe them.

> *(The white noise assaults the theater again. Only A reacts to it and exits/disappears. The noise is switched off.*
> *Silence.*
> *C enters/appears carrying a small flower arrangement.)*

C: Surely not surprised.
B: Disappointed.
C: There's always hope.
B: Not always. Nothing is always.
C: So, how is…
B: Depends on what the definition of the word "is" is.

> *(Silence.)*

C: How are…
B: Fine.
C: A word that tells me nothing.
B: We're big on nothing around here. In fact, you could say we're rather keen on it.
C: "Rather keen on it." Funny phrase. Sounds English. Like England English.
B: Maybe it is. Doesn't matter. You understand what I mean. It is our shared language. Our… common tongue.
C: Sounds upper class. Posh. Something from the mouth of the aristocracy.
B: I wouldn't know.
C: I'll have to take your word on that.
B: What do you want?
C: Information. To know…
B: Current physical condition? Mental health?
C: Yes.
B: A report? An executive summary? A briefing?
C: A conversation.
B: An exchange of information.
C: Yes.
B: Knowledge. Opinions…
C: Yes.
B: But I don't care what you think.
C: I know. That's not important.
B: I could just lie to you.
C: A possibility.
B: You'd never know.
C: I would eventually. The truth always comes out.
B: Always, again. You like always. The idea of it
C: It's a comfort
B: Always and forever.
C: And why not?
B: It's not true. It's a farce. It's a lie.
C: It helps.
B: "The truth always come out."
C: Touché.

(Silence.)
B: So? Ask your questions.
C: May I see???
B: No. You may not.
C: So, now you're the gatekeeper.
B: For the moment.
C: This was agreed to? Doesn't sound like…
B: I'm here now. I know what's best.
C: And what's that?
B: No disturbances.
C: You don't need to be afraid of me…
B: I'm not.
C: Or jealous.
B: Please go.
C: Tell me what happened and then I'll leave.
B: What did you hear?
C: Nothing specific… Someone called an ambulance… Late morning visit to the ER…
B: Late morning? Sounds specific to me.
C: That's what I heard.
B: We're very private people.
C: Paint it for me in broad strokes.
    (Silence.)
B: What you heard sums it up nicely. Late morning visit to the emergency room. Wasn't admitted and sent home.
C: What happened? A fall? Chest pain? TIA?
B: …
C: A small stroke?
B: I don't know. They don't know yet. They haven't decided.
C: What does…
B: Doesn't remember.
    (A enters/appears. A is unsteady.)
C: Well, hello.
A: What?
C: What's the matter?
A: What do you want?
C: You remember me.
A: Of course.
C: We had some good times.
A: I remember the bad.
C: Surely you remember…
A: I remember things that happened. But when I do it's like looking at a photograph of other people. Like an ad in a magazine.
B: Defense mechanism.
A: Like traumatized people and amnesia.
C: C'mon, now… Traumatized?

A: That's how I remember it.

C: I think that's more than a bit self-serving and unduly harsh.

A: What would you call it? How do you remember things?

C: Some were hard. But some were good — even very good. I brought you these for the good times.

(C holds out the flowers.)

A: I don't remember any.

(Silence.

A takes the flowers.

The white noise assaults the theater again. This time, the white noise gives birth to a horrible, metallic howl; a feral snarl of metal grinding against metal-against-metal scream. It visibly paralyzes A before the sound is abruptly switched off.

B and C move to assist A, who backs away from both.)

A: What do you want?

B: Are you all right?

C: What just happened?

(Silence.)

A: I don't know you.

B: It's OK...

A: I don't know you either.

B: That's not funny.

A: No, it's not. I don't know... I don't remem... Tell me who you are.

B: You know...

A: Remind me. Please.

B: You don't have to be scared.

A: I'm not.

B: Except maybe of them.

C: Me?

B: Who else? Certainly not me.

A: Just... stay where you are. Please.

B: All right.

C: Okay.

A: I need to figure this out.

C: What do you need to know?

A: I live here.

C: That's right.

A: *(To C.)* And you don't.

B: Also correct. But I do live here.

A: With me?

B: Yes.

A: *(To C.)* Is that the truth?

B: Now, you're scaring me.

(Silence.)

A: How long?

B: What?

A: Have we lived together?
B: Well, it's been…
A: What kind of… of arrangement is it?
B: It's not an arrangement. It's a mutually beneficial association.
A: Like minds?
B: I believe so.
A: Physically?
B: Yes. That, too.
A: I see. Or rather, I understand — but I don't see…
B: Calm down.
A: I don't want to calm down.
B: You need to…
A: Or what? What will you do?
B: Nothing to you. Only for you.
A: Such as?
B: Help you calm down.
A: Are you threatening me?
B: God, no… I'm not…
C: How about a cup of tea? Or a drink?
B: Stay out of this.
C: Yes, how about a good, strong drink?
A: What do you mean by "this?"
B: Excuse me?
A: The "this" they're staying out of.
B: Our conversation. Our situation. Our lives.
A: I don't like this conversation, I don't know what the situation is, and I don't remember our lives.
C: It's not important.
A: It's very important to me.
B: I told you to stay out of this.
C: You can't tell me what to do…
B: You're making things worse. Can't you see that?
C: Maybe he/she prefers that I be here.
B: Not instead of me.
C: Maybe. Maybe not.
B: He/she doesn't know what they want — he/she remembers nothing.
C: Let's ask and find out.
B: They don't have enough information to know — to make a decision like that.
A: Whoever you are… Whoever you claim to be… Stop talking about me as if I weren't in the room. I'm here. I know that much. I'm here. I just don't know where here is.
C: Sorry. How can I help?
B: By leaving.
C: *(To A.)* Is that what you want? Tell me that's what you want and I'll go. I'll come back later to check up on you.
A: Why would you do that?

C: Because I care. Oh, yes — I still care about what happens to you.

A: Why?

C: I used to live here.

A: The three of us???

C: No, only you and me. That's what I thought, anyway. What I believed. That it was just the two of us.

A: But there were more people involved.

C: That's one way to put it.

B: *(To C.)* How would you put it?

C: I already said: there were more people involved. I just didn't know that... Until I did. And when I did, I left.

B: Best thing for everyone.

A: Including me?

B: Best thing for you is to go back to the ER right now.

A: No...

B: That's what they said the last time we were there: if it happens again you need to go straight back to the hospital. I don't expect you remember...

A: I don't.

B: Well, I do.

A: So you say.

B: I'm going to call the ambulance...

A: No, don't...

B: The golden hour — do you remember about that?

A: I haven't had a stroke.

B: You don't know that. And that's the point — you don't know because you can't remember anything. Does that sound normal to you? You want to ignore that?

C: I'll drive you.

B: We're wasting time. He/she needs immediate care. Professional care. He/she needs an ambulance.

A: Don't call.

B: That's what you said the first time.

A: I don't remember!

B: Which is why I'm calling!

A: I can't afford it!

B: Don't worry about that. You can't worry about...

A: You didn't see the bill!

    (Silence.)

B: You saw the bill?

A: Yes.

B: You remember the bill for an ambulance?

    (Silence.)

A: I suppose I do. It was for over eight-hundred dollars.

    (Silence.)

A: *(Cont.)* And that was after insurance paid.

C: Remarkable.

A: You're damn right. Eight hundred dollars for a ride.

C: I mean it's remarkable that you remember.

A: It came in the mail today. I have it here somewhere...

B: I guess money still leaves an impression. *(To C.)* You don't. And I don't. But money does.

A: I'm sorry — that's what I remember. I thought you'd be happy that I remembered anything at all.

B: I am happy. I am relieved you remember the bill for the ambulance.

C: Is that all you remember?

A: I don't know. How can I know if I've forgotten something?

C: Good point.

B: That's enough.

C: Who are you? The Memory Police?

B: You need to go now...

C: And yet here I still am.

B: I'll throw you out if you don't go.

C: I'll go if he/she wants me to. *(To A.)* Do you want me to go?

A: I don't know!

B: *(To C.)* Don't do that!

C: I didn't do anything.

B: You're upsetting him/her. Asking questions when you know they don't know the answer.

C: Maybe he/she does know.

B: How can he/she know if they can't remember?

C: Maybe he/she just needs to be asked before they'll remember. Something to trigger the brain.

B: And maybe we shouldn't be triggering his/her brain! Maybe that's causing harm.

C: You don't know that.

B: No, I don't. That's why we need to get back to the hospital so that someone qualified can help.

A: What happened to my Japanese Maple tree?

   (Silence.)

B: What?

A: I had a Japanese Maple tree right out there in the middle of the front yard. *(To B.)* I did, didn't I? *(To C.)* Didn't I?

   (The white noise assaults the theater again. This time, the white noise gives birth to a horrible, metallic howl; a feral snarl of metal grinding against metal-against-metal scream. It visibly paralyzes A before the sound is abruptly switched off. The lights fade to black.)

   (Curtain.)

Socky Tells All

Rollin Jewett

Characters

Andy: *childlike, 17-25 years of age*
Nurse Todd: *kind, professional, 20's to 40's*
Dr. Baxter: *heavyset, 30's to 60's*

Setting

Day, Mental Institution, Patient Room.
The room is small with a bed, dresser, desk with reading lamp, and a wooden chair. Next to the bed is a small night table. There's a window upstage center with bars on the outside. The door to the room has a small window with mesh wire. Next to the door is a buzzer that the patient can ring for service.

Scene

(Andy sits in bed reading a comic book. He's a prisoner of sorts — a patient in the Whispering Oaks Sanitarium, a private mental health institution. In the crook of his arm is a small sock monkey he calls "Socky." There's a knock on the door.)

Andy: *(To Socky.)* Company, Socky. *(Loudly.)* Entre-vous!
(Nurse Todd enters carrying an assortment of fresh linens. She's attractive, though somewhat severe-looking in her uniform. She has a cordial, but professional manner.)
Nurse Todd: Good morning, Andy. Did you sleep well?
Andy: Oh, yes, Nurse Todd. Thank you. Socky had a bit of a coughing fit and woke me up... but I was able to get back to sleep all right.
(Nurse Todd gives him a sharp look, places a few linens on the desk and goes into the bathroom.)
Nurse Todd: *(From bathroom.)* I hope you're not going to start with that "Socky" business when Dr. Baxter comes to check on you.
(She comes out of the bathroom with some crumpled towels.)
Nurse Todd: This is something of a decisive opportunity for you, Andy. Dr. Baxter is an important man in this institution. I hope you realize the extent to which your behavior with him today can help or hinder your release.

Andy: *(To Socky.)* You hear that, Socky? If we're good, they'll let us out of here. Then we can go out and play with the grown-ups. Won't that be fun?

(He makes Socky shake his head "no.")

Andy: Oh, come on now, Sock. Don't be like that. We'll be good, won't we?

(He shakes Socky's head "no." Nurse Todd throws the towels on the floor in a heap.)

Nurse Todd: Now, you've got to stop that, Andy! I'm serious! Dr. Baxter will be here shortly and if he sees you talking to that stuffed monkey, it might spoil your chances. Let me have those sheets now.

(Andy gets off the bed, holding Socky.)

Andy: What's this one like?

(Nurse Todd takes off Andy's sheets and tosses them in the pile. She puts on new sheets as she talks.)

Nurse Todd: Oh, he seems qualified enough, I suppose. A little on the plump side, about fifty. In addition to being the new chief-of-staff, he's also head of the out-patient program, Andy. That's why you've got to be at your best.

Andy: Why hasn't he been by to check on us before?

Nurse Todd: Well, Andy... he's only been here a month and a half. He's been very busy... learning our procedures and familiarizing himself with the books and staff.

Andy: Familiarizing himself! *(Laughs.)* And what happened to that nice Dr. Gavinski? Why hasn't he been by to see us?

Nurse Todd: Now, Andy... you were right there when he had the... break-down. I suppose he's resting somewhere.

Andy: Oh. That's too bad. We liked him, didn't we, Socky?

(He shakes Socky's head "no." Nurse Todd turns to him sharply.)

Nurse Todd: Look, Andy... I want to give you some advice. You're a smart boy. I don't think there's much wrong with you and I've said as much to Dr. Baxter. But you're going to have to do your part. If you want to get out of here... and soon... you're going to have to stop this... Socky crap.

Andy: *(Feigning shock.)* You hear that, Socky? Nurse Todd said a naughty word. *(Places his hands over Socky's ears.)* Naughty, naughty, naughty!

(Nurse Todd throws up her hands. She picks up the towels and linens and heads to the door.)

Nurse Todd: Andy... you're going to blow it again. I don't know why you have to start this every time a new doctor comes to see you. You've been here two years now and there's not a thing wrong with you. *(Shakes her head.)* Well, it's out of my hands. I just wish you'd stop and think about what you're doing. It's such a waste.

(Andy sulks. She goes to him.)

Nurse Todd: Now look... I may not be here much longer. There have been some changes in the way things are run... and in the staff. I just don't want to see you get hurt, when you might be better off...

(He lays his head against her shoulder. She pets him a moment, then presses the buzzer. The door buzzes and she leaves. Andy jumps back on the bed with Socky.)

Andy: Don't pay any attention to her, Socky. We know what we're doing...

don't we? *(Nods Socky's head.)* You're the only one who understands me, Sock.
(He kisses the monkey and picks up the comic book. A knock on the door is heard.)
Andy: Entre-vous!
(Dr. Baxter enters. He's a big man with a benevolent air and carries himself with great dignity. He holds a file in his hand — presumably Andy's.)
Dr. Baxter: *(Smiling.)* Well, hello, Andrew. Or do you prefer Andy?
Andy: *(Smiling back.)* Whatever makes you more comfortable.
(Dr. Baxter moves to the bed and holds out his hand to Andy.)
Dr. Baxter: Well, I heard the nurse refer to you as Andy... so that's what I'll call you.
Andy: *(Shaking his hand.)* All right, sir. And I'll call you Benjamin. Or do you prefer Benjy?
Dr. Baxter: *(A little surprised.)* Ah... Benjamin. But most everyone in the hospital calls me Dr. Baxter.
Andy: Socky says there are a few who call you Benjy.
Dr. Baxter: *(Perplexed.)* Who says?
Andy: Socky. *(Pretends introductions.)* Socky... Benjy. Benjy... Socky. There. Now that we're all best friends and everything, why don't you sit down and we can hash it out and shoot the bull.
Dr. Baxter: *(Lightening up.)* Ah... very well. Thank you, Andy. I will.
(He pulls the wooden chair up to the bed and straddles it, his arms across the back of the chair.)
Dr. Baxter: I've heard some very encouraging things about you, Andy. Your progress has been quite remarkable considering your background. You pose very little problem to the staff — they seem to like you. You seem a model patient from most reports. Oh, I know there's been some trouble between you and a few of the doctors in the past, but nothing to worry about. Overall, your character seems pretty sound. I like that.
Andy: Well, sir... the staff is to be commended. They're a great bunch. Especially Nurse Todd. She's the cat's pajamas. Don't you think, sir?
Dr. Baxter: *(Insincerely.)* Nurse Todd... yes. She's very... professional. Indeed.
Andy: *(To Socky.)* We like her best, don't we, Socky? Socky says he likes your tie.
Dr. Baxter: I didn't know you had a little... friend.
Andy: Didn't you read my file?
Dr. Baxter: Well... not entirely. But... there's nothing too wrong with having a little friend.
(He leans forward as if to tell some great secret.)
Dr. Baxter: We all talk to ourselves from time to time. *(Conspiratorially.)* Even me.
(He winks at Andy. Andy winks back.)
Andy: Socky says he'd wink, too... but he can't close his eyes.
Dr. Baxter: *(Laughs.)* That must get rather tiring after awhile, eh?
Andy: *(Seriously.)* Well, sir, the problem with not being able to close your eyes is that you see everything — all the time. Even if you don't want to. Do you know what I mean, sir?
Dr. Baxter: *(Feigning interest.)* Well, no, Andy... not exactly.
Andy: That's because you're a grown-up and you can close your eyes.
Dr. Baxter: I'm afraid I don't follow you, Andy.

(Andy leans forward.)

Andy: Well, you see, sir... Socky sees all, so he knows all. And he can't keep a secret, so do you know what he does, sir?

Dr. Baxter: *(Fascinated.)* What?

Andy: He tells all. To me.

Dr. Baxter: What do you mean?

Andy: *(Shakes his head.)* He tells me everything, sir. And I can hardly believe some of it. For instance, he's just told me that you had wheat toast and orange marmalade for breakfast. Oh... and a cup of black coffee.

Dr. Baxter: *(Amazed.)* Why, yes. That's right. *(Checks his suit.)* Did I spill something? Ah... Nurse Todd must have told you. But that's very clever, Andy.

Andy: *(Listening to Socky.)* What's that, Socky? He put something in his coffee? Whiskey? No, Socky, it can't be.

Dr. Baxter: That's not amusing, Andy. Now why don't you put your little friend away while we talk about your future.

Andy: Oh, no, sir. Socky gets very angry if left out. He can be very vengeful when he wants to be.

Dr. Baxter: Very well. Now, Andy, I have some news that might make you very happy.

Andy: *(Excited.)* Are we going to stay here forever?

Dr. Baxter: *(Put off.)* Well, no... that wasn't exactly the news I was going to tell you, Andy. *(Beat.)* Why? Would it make you happy to stay here?

Andy: Oh, yes, sir. Socky and I are very happy here. It's become our home. And there's no place like home, right, sir?

Dr. Baxter: Yes... but this is not your home, Andy.

Andy: It is so, isn't it, Socky? Socky says it is and Socky never lies. Only people lie.

Dr. Baxter: Of course... this is your home for now, Andy. But you're getting better... and very soon now, you'll be able to go to your real home. Won't you like that?

Andy: Oh, no, sir. They mistreated me there and... well, sir, if you'd read my file, you'd know they're the reason why I'm here. They made me crazy. They beat me and lied to me, you know. I don't want to go back, sir. Ever.

Dr. Baxter: Now, now, Andy. Things have changed. Your parents are very nice people and they care a great deal about you. I've met them. Simple folk to be sure, but... nice.

Andy: Oh, no sir. You don't know them like I do. They're rotten through and through.

Dr. Baxter: They've changed, Andy. They've gotten counseling for their behavior. Give them a chance. You haven't seen them in a long time.

Andy: *(Bitterly.)* Ha! They're grown-ups. They never change.

Dr. Baxter: Not all grown-ups are rotten, Andy. I think if you gave me a chance, you'd like me.

Andy: *(Slow smile.)* Socky says he heard Nurse Randall call you Benjy yesterday. He says you were being naughty with her.

Dr. Baxter: *(Taken aback.)* Wha!? I won't stand for insolence, young man. Now, I hope you'll change your attitude and behave properly. I'm trying to help you.

(Andy bursts out laughing, then tries to hide it.)

Dr. Baxter: What's so funny?

113

Andy: Socky says you don't want to help us. He says you want to get rid of us. He says you were hired to get rid of all us poor crazies in order to make room for the rich crazies.

Dr. Baxter: *(Off-guard.)* That's enough, Andrew. I don't know how you could possibly... I mean, that's absurd. How on earth did you think up such a preposterous idea?

Andy: *(To Socky.)* You were right, Socky. See how defensive he is? He doesn't care about us. He takes his orders from greedy Ms. Nigel, the founder. I bet she sweetened his salary.

Dr. Baxter: *(Rising.)* That's not true!

(He paces away.)

Andy: Socky says it is and I trust Socky. I don't trust you!

Dr. Baxter: I don't know where you're getting your information, but it's a complete fabrication. In fact, I took a pay cut in order to come here. I go where I'm needed.

Andy: Socky says you were fired from your last job. Something about getting caught with one of the nurses. And there you were yesterday with Nurse Randall. *(Clucks his tongue.)* Up to your old tricks again, eh? And you a married man. I'm glad Nurse Todd didn't give in to you. Even though you threatened her with her job.

(Dr. Baxter crosses to him.)

Dr. Baxter: *(Noticeably perturbed.)* I won't have this, Andy. I simply won't stand for it. This is all some silly gossip you've overheard. Your accusations are completely unfounded and this is really a very poor joke. *(Sadly.)* I'm extremely disappointed in you, Andrew. I had heard that you were a well-mannered, good-natured young man. But I find your behavior very disturbing and I shall speak to the staff about your reports.

Andy: If there's any staff left.

Dr. Baxter: What do you mean?

Andy: You know very well what I mean, sir. Socky says you've already fired four people since you've been here. Two of them were nurses who wouldn't sleep with you. Socky says that Ms. Nigel told you to cut costs. He says she's a money-grubbing bitch and you're nothing but a lecherous administrative puppet!

Dr. Baxter: *(Incredulous.)* I don't believe this... how could you possibly...

(He fights for composure. After a moment, he turns and shakes his finger at Andy.)

Dr. Baxter: Ah-ha...ah-ha. I know what you're trying to do. You want me to believe that you're psychologically unsound. That's why you're saying all these horrible things. Very clever, Andy. You've got a wonderful imagination, my boy. But it's not going to work. I don't believe there's a thing wrong with you and I'm going to make sure you're released as soon as possible.

Andy: *(Screaming.)* We don't want to be released!

Dr. Baxter: *(Gaining the upper hand.)* I'm afraid you have no choice in the matter, young man. All it takes is a signature and a phone call to your guardians.

Andy: But they don't care about us! They're just like you! They lie to us and cheat us! Just like you cheat the hospital by changing the ledger and making checks out to a special fund — the Dr. Baxter fund!

(Dr. Baxter's jaw drops. He walks slowly, menacingly toward Andy.)

Dr. Baxter: Where did you hear that? Tell me, you little monster! No one could've seen me... I was very careful. Now... where did you hear it?!

Andy: *(Yelling.)* Socky told me!

Dr. Baxter: *(Closer.)* Liar! Crazy goddamn liar! I want to know the truth, you little bastard. How did you find out about the books? I was alone in my office. How?!

(He stands over Andy who cowers on the bed, tightly clutching Socky.)

Andy: Socky!

(Dr. Baxter slaps him.)

Dr. Baxter: Tell me again.

Andy: Socky!

(Dr. Baxter slaps him again. Andy is sobbing now.)

Dr. Baxter: One more time...

Andy: Socky...

(Dr. Baxter grabs Socky from him and throws him across the room.)

Andy: *(Horrified.)* Socky!

(Andy jumps off the bed and almost gets past Dr. Baxter, who grabs him forcefully. He's considerably larger than Andy, who struggles vainly.)

Dr. Baxter: (Beside himself, calmly.) Now... once more, young man. Before I lose my temper. Who told you about the books... and Nurse Randall and the rest? And if you say Socky again, I'll snap your neck and claim you attacked me. How did you know?

(Andy elbows him in the stomach. Dr. Baxter lets go and doubles over. Andy pushes him on the bed and runs to the door.)

Andy: Help! Help!

(He rings the buzzer over and over. Dr. Baxter has recovered and moves to Andy. He grabs him and puts his hands around Andy's throat. He bends him back over the desk and begins to strangle him.

Nurse Todd's face appears in the door window. She sees what's happening and quickly opens the door.)

Nurse Todd: *(Calling out.)* Dr. Baxter... stop! Stop!

(Dr. Baxter lets go of Andy and runs to the sock monkey. He picks it up, hugging it defensively. He laughs wildly, mocking Andy.)

Dr. Baxter: Ha! You don't have any witnesses now, Andy! You can't prove anything! You can't prove anything! Ha ha ha! You can't prove anything!

(He runs out of the room, clutching Socky, still laughing maniacally.)

Nurse Todd: Are you okay, Andy?

(He nods. She runs after Dr. Baxter. Andy closes the door. He goes to his bed, reaches underneath it and pulls out a duplicate sock monkey which he places carefully on the bed.)

Andy: (To Sock Monkey, finger pressed to lips.) Shhhhh....

(He then goes to his dresser against the wall and moves it. Behind the dresser is a panel, which Andy removes, revealing a cut out hole in the wall. He crawls through the hole, replaces the panel... and is gone.)

(Curtain.)

Midnight Snack

Evan Baughfman

Characters

Figure/Sebastian Queen: *famous horror author, sneaking around in the dark*
Julia: *head librarian; frustrated and finally taking things into her own hands*

Props

Scary mask, backpack, smartphone, jar of pickled pigs' feet, book drop

Setting

Midnight, outside a small city library at the book drop.

Scene

(A Figure in a black hoodie quickly surveys the dark scene and then approaches the book drop, near the front entrance door. The Figure also wears a scary rubber mask, completely concealing his or her face.
Once at the book drop, the Figure removes a jar from a backpack. The Figure opens the book drop, ready to place the jar inside of it, when…
Julia, a librarian dressed in dark clothing herself, steps from the shadows behind the Figure. Julia shines a flashlight right at the Figure's back.)

Julia: Step away from the book drop!
(The Figure, jar in hand, freezes in the flashlight's beam, book drop still open.)
Listen! I… I have a gun!
(Julia has no gun, but the Figure doesn't know this and slowly closes the book drop.)
Thanks for… for not slamming that!
(The Figure begins to step away from the book drop…)
Hey! Hey, wait a sec!
(The Figure freezes in place again.)
Could you, um, put that jar down on the ground, at your feet? *(As the Figure puts the jar down, Julia says…)* Now… uh… Move back a few steps! Toward my voice!

116

Figure: How many steps?

    (The Figure's voice, male, is muffled beneath the mask.)

Julia: I said, a few!

Figure: People have different interpretations of "few." Others might think it means "five or six," while you might think it means "three or four."

Julia: "Three or four" is "some," not "few."

Figure: Don't want to be shot in the back because I took more steps than you were expecting me to take.

Julia: A "few" is like "five or six"... isn't it?

Figure: That's what I've always thought. Now, what is it exactly you want me to do? Five or six steps?

Julia: Five steps back, toward my voice.

    (The Figure is about to take his first step back toward Julia's voice, but then he stops himself.)

Figure: And how large should my steps be? I don't want you to think I'm rushing toward you and end up with a hole in the back of my head.

Julia: I... I don't know how large each of your steps should be.

Figure: You don't know...?

Julia: Why're you annoyed with me? You are the one shoving garbage in the book drop every freaking night!

Figure: I'll explain. Just don't shoot.

Julia: Okay. Take some steps back first.

Figure: "Some" steps? I thought you said "a few"...?

Julia: I... uh... I changed my mind. Take... take... three steps back, toward my voice, please. Three steps, at your normal stride. You're not long-jumping here.

Figure: Okay, here I go. Ready?

Julia: Ready.

    (The Figure takes three relatively-normal steps backward.)

Good. Now, remove your mask.

Figure: I'd really prefer not to.

Julia: It's getting harder to understand you under that thing. Now, do it. Or... I'll place you under arrest.

Figure: You're not a police officer. If you were, you would've already announced yourself as one. And you really shouldn't impersonate one, either. That's quite illegal.

Julia: I... I'm a security guard.

Figure: I don't think the city prioritizes overnight security at a library. Are you a concerned citizen?

    (Julia doesn't answer.)

Ma'am, I don't want to alarm you, but there are security cameras out here recording us at this very moment. Cameras showing you performing an illegal act. Those same cameras are the reason I don't want to show my face.

Julia: The cameras don't work. They haven't worked for two weeks.

Figure: How would you know that?

Julia: I'm Julia Jones, head librarian. And... And... if the city's not willing to do it... I will do whatever it takes to keep my library safe and clean! You hear me? WHATEVER IT TAKES! As you can see, you've driven me a little bit off the deep end here! Now, turn around and take off that mask! The only one who'll see your face is me!

Figure: But—

Julia: Do it now! NOW!

(The Figure puts his hands up and slowly turns around. Julia shines the flashlight right in his masked face.)

Figure: Mind not shining that thing in my eyes?

Julia: YES! TAKE OFF THE MASK!

(The Figure removes the mask, revealing that he's a fifty-something-year-old man. This is world-renowned horror author, Sebastian Queen.)

Sebastian: Hi.

Julia: Oh... Oh, my God... You're... You're...

Sebastian: Looks like you might know who I am... I'll introduce myself anyway. I'm Sebastian.

Julia: Why is WORLD-FAMOUS AUTHOR, Sebastian Queen, using my library as his own personal dumpster?!

Sebastian: Lower the light just a little?

(Julia lowers the flashlight beam and Sebastian sees that she doesn't have a weapon.)

You don't even have a gun?! Well, that was awfully mean of you!

Julia: You put fried chicken into my book drop Sunday night! Monday night, it was chow mein! Tuesday, it was three Big Macs! Wednesday, chicken enchiladas! Last night, a full sleeve of Oreos! And tonight...!

(She shines a light on the jar behind Sebastian.)

What is that?

Sebastian: Pickled pigs' feet.

Julia: Pickled pigs' feet! Why?!

Sebastian: I could leave right now, and no one would ever believe I was here, least of all the actual police. If you tried to tell anyone about this, about me... they'd think you were nuts.

(While Sebastian talks, Julia's removes her phone from her pocket. She snaps a photo of him. The camera flash is blinding.)

Sebastian: Come on! Really?

Julia: Calm down. I should've done that earlier. Now I have proof. If the police don't find that interesting, God knows Facebook will.

Sebastian: Please, don't post that.

Julia: Then explain to me why a bestselling, multi-millionaire author has been sneaking around my little library for the past week!

Sebastian: I've been trying to feed your library, alright? Give it a midnight snack.

Julia: WHAT?!

Sebastian: Your library is a living thing now. It needs to eat.

Julia: That's your explanation? Seriously?

Sebastian: I've seen this kind of thing all over the world, I promise you.

Julia: Hungry libraries of Earth.

Sebastian: Yes. I — and other horror authors — do our due diligence as makers of the macabre to ensure that possessed libraries everywhere are satisfied.

Julia: Oh, the library's "possessed" now, too? Is that right?

Sebastian: Well, that's technically why it's alive. And I'd wager it's been possessed for a while. You just didn't know about it until now.

Julia: You "makers of the macabre" — you placate possessed libraries all around the globe by... by feeding them enchiladas?

Sebastian: Not every library is partial to Mexican food. Obviously.

Julia: Obviously.

Sebastian: It's part of our responsibility to do this. Our service. We put enough scary stuff out into the world, so the least we can do is keep some of the real horror at bay.

Julia: Uh huh... And which other writers are we talking about here?

(Sebastian smiles, shaking his head.)

Sebastian: I know how farfetched this sounds, but it's the truth. Each library houses thousands of books, right? It is therefore not outside the realm of possibility that, on occasion, a library will accidentally come into ownership of a haunted or cursed manuscript. If that book is opened, its trapped spirit or demon is released, and—

Julia: Demon?!

Sebastian: Yes. That spirit, demon, entity... whatever you want to call it... That thing will escape the pages of its open book and, no longer confined, will take over the entire building. You mentioned that the security cameras aren't working?

Julia: Right. They aren't. But they rarely work.

Sebastian: I've come into your library a few times over the last week, and I've noticed other things not working. Flickering lights over the stacks. Toilets out of service. Computers on the fritz. I saw the need to intervene.

Julia: You've been inside this library and no one's noticed you?

Sebastian: I wore a disguise.

(Julia looks to the mask.)

I wasn't wearing the mask, okay? Now, whatever's taken over your library is making things problematic for you and your patrons. Have you noticed anything strange at all going on lately? Books falling off the shelves inexplicably? Voices that don't seem to belong to anyone in particular? The heater not being especially effective against the cold outside?

Julia: I've noticed... things.

Sebastian: The possession's why. A library's supposed to be a positive space. A place of relaxation and comfort, wouldn't you say?

Julia: Of course.

Sebastian: Whenever I visit a town for the first time, I look for the local library, because that's where I go to escape... decompress... from the real world. I'm staying nearby for the next few weeks, working on a new novel.

(Sebastian points to the front entrance.)

Whenever I step foot in there, I know something's amiss.

Julia: So you've decided to feed the… the demonic library.

Sebastian: No one's happy when they're hungry. They get grumpy… angry…

Julia: You're telling me, the backed-up toilets aren't a plumbing issue. The library's just "hangry"?

Sebastian: If you want your library to function at its best, it needs sustenance. It's an important part of the community and needs to be maintained. It shouldn't turn on its patrons… turn them away with its… misbehaviors. And it won't, so long as it's fed.

Julia: But we keep finding the food you leave behind in the book drop. The library… the demon… ghost… It's not eating what you're trying to feed it.

(Sebastian shrugs.)

Sebastian: Must be a picky eater. That's why I've tried so many different things.

(Julia gestures to the jar.)

Julia: But… pickled pigs' feet?

Sebastian: Some libraries have particular tastes. Peculiar palates.

Julia: Why don't you and your secret cabal of authors just exorcise what's in these buildings? Why feed them and allow them to stay at all? At the very least, trap them back inside their books.

Sebastian: Exorcisms are… dangerous. So is trying to get these things back into their spellbound tomes. Libraries can… resist with a plethora of force… violence. By feeding your beast, I'm keeping it calm. If we aren't careful… don't quell its hunger soon… this library could rip free of its foundation and terrorize the city. Nothing would be able to stop it.

Julia: "Terrorize the city"…?

Sebastian: Imagine an irritable building barreling down the street, smashing everything in sight.

(Sebastian stomps around, mimicking a giant monster.)

Now, imagine that same building full of books on every subject imaginable, making it literally the smartest thing alive in the area. How would the authorities be able to contain such a monster?

Julia: Has a library ever… ever "ripped free of its foundation"?

Sebastian: The media usually blames the actions of disgruntled libraries on tornadoes.

(Julia lets this all sink in for a few moments.)

Julia: I mean… wow. It's incredible. Bravo. An interesting story, but…

Sebastian: Not a story. Fact.

(Behind Sebastian, the front entrance door slams open! A booming, animalistic ROAR explodes from within the library.)

See? It wants its snack.

(Julia is stunned. Sebastian picks up the jar, places it into Julia's trembling hands.)

You say you care about this library. Well, it's feeding time. What do you say?

(Julia nods. She walks over to the book drop, hesitates. The library ROARS at her again.)

Julia: Okay, okay! Here, you go! Here's your jar of pigs' feet! Open wide!

(Julia places the jar into the drop. Closes it shut, tight. The library falls silent.)

Sebastian: Good job. You and this library... You're going to be closer than ever now. If it likes the pigs' feet, you're going to have to get it some more jars. They sell them right down at the—

(The library suddenly BELCHES, thunderously. Julia covers her ears.)

Well, that was rude. The pigs' feet... Yeah... A few jars at a time should probably do.

(Curtain.)

Night Picnic Nominations
for the 2022 Pushcart Prize:

Shane Delaney, *The Starlight Lounge* (fiction)

RC de Winter, *scuppered* (poem)

Philip Gambone, *The Hazardous Life* (fiction)

Ivana Mestrovic, *A Short Story About Love* (poem)

Paula Reed Nancarrow, *Bodie Bride* (poem)

Carla Ward, *The Garden* (fiction)

Printed in Great Britain
by Amazon

87778324R00071